PEARSON

HUMAN SEXUALITY

Pruitt, Allegrante, Prothrow-Stith

TEACHER'S EDITION

Master essential health skills with these new features!

Updated highlights include

- Current information on building healthy relationships, including dating and online friendships
- Digital Courseware, including eTexts and online resources
- Up-to-date statistics and data throughout the program

D1243625

WITHDRAWN

Glenview, Illinois • Boston, Massachusetts • Chandler, Arizona • Upper Saddle River, New Jersey

ALWAYS LEARNING

PEARSON

PEARSON

HUMAN SEXUALITY

This work is protected by United States copyright laws and is provided *solely for the use of teachers and administrators* in teaching courses and assessing student learning in their classes and schools. Dissemination or sale of any part of this work (including on the World Wide Web) will destroy the integrity of the work and is *not* permitted.

Acknowledgments appear on p. 120, which constitutes an extension of this copyright page.

Copyright © 2014 Pearson Education, Inc., or its affiliates. All Rights Reserved. Printed in the United States of America. This publication is protected by copyright, and permission should be obtained from the publisher prior to any prohibited reproduction, storage in a retrieval system, or transmission in any form or by any means, electronic, mechanical, photocopying, recording, or likewise. For information regarding permissions, write to Rights Management & Contracts, Pearson Education, Inc., Upper Saddle River, New Jersey 07458.

Pearson is a trademark, in the U.S. and/or other countries, of Pearson Education, Inc., or its affiliates.

Discovery Education™ is a trademark of Discovery Communications, Inc., used under license. The Discovery Education logo is a trademark of Discovery Communications, Inc.

Use of the trademarks implies no relationship, sponsorship, endorsement, sale, or promotion on the part of Pearson Education, Inc., or its affiliates.

PEARSON

ISBN-13: 978-0-13-327531-5
ISBN-10: 0-13-327531-0
1 2 3 4 5 6 7 8 9 10 V092 18 17 16 15 14 13

Introduction to *Pearson Human Sexuality*

The purpose of this text is to provide students with an accurate understanding of the important topic of human sexuality. Only with this understanding can students integrate their sexuality into their lives in healthy and fulfilling ways. This is true both at present, as they experience puberty, and throughout their lives, as they make decisions about sexual behavior and reproductive health.

Any decision is best made if it is informed. *Pearson Human Sexuality* informs in a clear, engaging, and objective way. It also provides opportunities for students to think about and share their opinions of and attitudes about human sexuality in an empathetic and nonjudgmental way.

Organization of the Text

The text is organized into five chapters that cover the major aspects of human sexuality. The chapter sequence is based on the pedagogical principle that responsible decision making, sexual or otherwise, should begin with a knowledge of basic facts. Therefore, the early chapters deal with the general concept of sexuality, and the structure and function of the male and female reproductive systems. The remaining chapters draw upon this body of knowledge to discuss dating and sexual decision making, family decisions, sexually transmitted infections, and issues of sexuality in society.

Pearson Human Sexuality reinforces the message of sexual abstinence by presenting abstinence as a normative, viable option for teens. It stresses the value of abstinence as a healthful behavior and teaches students the skills they need to choose abstinence.

Pearson Human Sexuality can be used as the main text for a course on human sexuality or as a supplement to a health or biology course. The basal text, along with the suggested activities in the Teacher's Edition, allows teachers to adapt the materials to a variety of course lengths. The variety of teaching strategies are aimed at students of different ability levels with multiple learning styles. This allows teachers to tailor their course to the time available, the specific curriculum requirements, and the needs and interests of students.

Creating a Supportive Classroom Environment

For a course on human sexuality to be a successful learning experience, students must feel secure and respected by their classmates and teacher. Only in this type of supportive atmosphere will students feel comfortable sharing their feelings and concerns about sexuality.

Whenever students reveal their views on personal issues, they risk being misunderstood, disagreed with, or even ridiculed by classmates. To prevent such negative outcomes, teachers must create an atmosphere of support, acceptance, and approval in the classroom. At the outset of the course, it may be helpful to establish some ground rules for making everyone feel comfortable and respected. Here are some examples.

- **Respect each other.** What each person has to say is important. Ridicule, teasing, and "put downs" will not be tolerated.
- **Listen to each other.** Listen respectfully and without interrupting when someone is speaking.
- **Use appropriate language.** When discussing reproductive structures and functions, use appropriate terminology. The use of slang terms is not allowed.
- **Discuss ideas, not people.** Ideas, impressions, questions, and, to some extent, opinions are appropriate for the classroom. But discussions about the individuals who express those ideas are inappropriate.
- **Avoid sharing highly personal experiences.** If personal experiences are to be shared, preface them with a phrase such as "I know of a situation where . . ." or "A friend of mine . . .," or submit them anonymously.

You may wish to create a poster listing the rules and display it in a prominent location in the classroom. Make it clear that everybody, including you, is expected to follow these rules at all times. Students should feel confident that you will enforce the rules.

Handling Sensitive Issues

Every chapter in *Pearson Human Sexuality* contains material that may cause embarrassment or discomfort. To aid teachers, each chapter in the Teacher's Edition of *Pearson Human Sexuality* includes sections titled Sensitive Issues. These clearly marked sections alert teachers to potentially sensitive topics and offer advice on how to approach the topics with special care.

At the start of the course, tell students that some of the topics may be embarrassing for them. You may want to acknowledge that you too may be uncomfortable with some topics. Some topics that will most likely cause student discomfort are

- questions about "normal" development.
- descriptions of the male and female reproductive systems.
- issues relating to sexual development, sexual arousal, and sexual orientation.
- discussions about HIV infection and AIDS.
- issues of self-protection and sexual assault.

In addition, students who have had personal experiences with other topics (for example, teen pregnancy, sexual abuse, homosexual experiences) may be very uncomfortable when the topic arises. To minimize student discomfort, teachers should try to be aware of students whose backgrounds may make them particularly sensitive to certain topics. Teachers should also be alert for signs of anxiety or discomfort on the part of students. Do not, at any time, pressure students to participate in class discussions that they do not wish to join or to reveal more than they are comfortable sharing. At the same time, emphasize that the class will provide understanding and support when a student does express personal concerns.

Throughout the course, it may be best to offer alternative ways for students to participate, such as writing in a journal, doing projects related to a topic, and doing independent readings or research. You may also want to place a “Question Box” in a prominent location in the classroom. Have students submit questions anonymously on topics of concern as they arise. You can then either set aside time each week to address the questions or integrate the questions into class discussions at the appropriate points in the course.

One particularly valuable teaching strategy for use with sensitive topics is role playing. Role plays offer students a safe way to practice handling difficult real-life situations. They also allow students to clarify their values and to try out different points of view. The roles, however, must be treated with sensitivity. For successful role plays, teachers should

- ask for volunteers.
- be careful not to cast students in roles they may identify with too closely.
- not allow the actors to become too emotionally involved in their roles.
- be alert for attacks on individual personalities and put an end to those attacks should they occur.
- summarize the activity by having students discuss what they have learned.

The challenge for teachers is to take these steps in an unobtrusive manner so that the role plays remain a student-directed activity.

Respecting Community Values

In every subject area, education is enhanced when there is cooperation between school, home, and the community. It’s a good idea to take the time to visit with community leaders, local clergy, and youth workers concerning their ideas about sexuality edcuation. For education about human sexuality to be effective, cooperation with and support from the community is essential.

School and District Policies As you plan your course, be sure to check with your school or district for any guidelines or recommendations for teaching about human sexuality. You need to know exactly what the policies are for your school. Also, find out if parental approval is necessary for the course, especially for potentially controversial subjects such as birth control and AIDS.

It is also advisable that you familiarize yourself with community attitudes about school-based sexuality education in general and about specific controversial topics. It is best to seek the approval of an administrator for any resources you are planning to use, such as videos and guest speakers. Discuss any school guidelines with speakers in advance.

Parental Involvement Parents and guardians have the right and responsibility to educate their children about sexuality. So, even if parental approval is not required in your school district, it makes sense to inform parents and guardians in advance about the sexuality curriculum. You should also offer parents an opportunity to review any of the materials you plan to use.

You can also support parental efforts by designing a course that respects the religious, cultural, and family values that students hold. Within a class, these values can be quite diverse. A tolerant attitude that acknowledges different viewpoints and value systems is best.

It is important to encourage students to discuss what they learn in your course with a parent or guardian. One way to foster student-parent communication is to make use of assignments like the *Health at Home* activities in the Student Edition. Through an open dialogue, parents will be able to impart their values and express their viewpoints about sensitive issues to their teens.

About the Authors

B. E. Pruitt

B. E. Pruitt, Ed.D., is Professor of Health Education at Texas A&M University. He served as executive director of the American Association for Health Education, and was the editor of the *American Journal of Health Education.* He has received numerous professional honors, including two National Professional Service Awards and the "Scholar" Award from the American Association for Health Education.

John P. Allegrante

John P. Allegrante, Ph.D., is Professor of Health Education and Deputy Provost at Teachers College and Adjunct Professor of Public Health in Sociomedical Sciences at Columbia University. A past president and Distinguished Fellow of the Society for Public Health Education, he is editor-in-chief of *Health Education & Behavior*. He received the Distinguished Career Award in Public Health Education and Health Promotion from the American Public Health Association.

Deborah Prothrow-Stith

Deborah Prothrow-Stith, M.D., is a Consultant with Spencer Stuart and Adjunct Professor of Practice at Harvard School of Public Health. As former Massachusetts Public Health Commissioner, she expanded HIV and substance abuse services. She is nationally recognized for her leadership in addressing violence as a public health problem and for her books *Murder Is No Accident* and *Sugar and Spice and No Longer Nice.*

Content Reviewers

Eric R. Buhi, Ph.D.
University of South Florida
Tampa, Florida

Elizabeth Coolidge-Stolz, M.D.
North Reading, Massachusetts

Jena Curtis, Ed.D.
State University of New York
College at Cortland
Cortland, New York

James P. Marshall, Ph.D.
Utah State University
Logan, Utah

Lisa M. Romero, Dr. P. H.
Centers for Disease Control and Prevention
Atlanta, Georgia

Health Educator Reviewers

Mike Code
Highlands High School
Fort Thomas, Kentucky

Elizabeth J. Godwin
Cape Coral High School
Cape Coral, Florida

Darrel Lang, Ed.D.
HIV/AIDS and Human Sexuality
Consultant
Kansas State Department of Education
Topeka, Kansas

Kathleen St. Laurent, R.N., M.S.N.
Coyle and Cassidy High School
Taunton, Massachusetts

Cristina Thyron
Prairie High School
Vancouver, Washington

Contents

TEENS Talk
Pictures of "Perfection"

CHAPTER 1

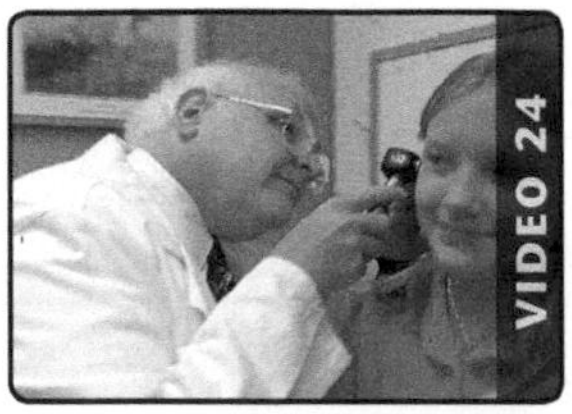

TEENS Talk
Taking Charge of Your Health

CHAPTER 2

TEENS Talk
Choosing Abstinence

CHAPTER 3

TEENS Talk

Teen Pregnancy

CHAPTER 4

TEENS Talk

Risks and STIs

CHAPTER 5

CHAPTER 1

Chapter Preview

Section 1 What Is Sexuality?
Teens experience a growing awareness of their sexuality. Family, the media, peers, and adult role models influence the development of sexuality. Sexuality is expressed in many ways. People do not have to be sexually active to express their sexuality.

Section 2 Concerns of Adolescence
Adolescence can be stressful, especially the changes to the reproductive system and development of secondary sex characteristics that accompany puberty. Building a strong self-concept requires a healthy body image, an understanding of emotions, and an acceptance of sexual feelings.

Section 3 Values and Responsibilities
With adolescence comes increased responsibilities and a greater understanding of values. What you value will influence your sexual decision-making, and can help you choose sexual abstinence. Talking things over with a trusted adult can help clarify your values. Finally, appreciating differences among your peers can help strengthen self-concept.

National Health Education Standards Correlation

1.12.2, 2.12.1, 2.12.2, 2.12.3, 2.12.5, 2.12.7, 2.12.8, 4.12.4, 5.12.2, 8.12.3,

CHAPTER 1

Understanding Sexuality

GO ONLINE PearsonSuccessNet.com

VIDEO 20

TEENS Talk

Pictures of "Perfection"

Preview **Activity**

What's Important to You?

Complete this activity before you watch the video.

1. Rank the following qualities by how important you think they are to *your* overall attractiveness (with 1 being most important).
   ____ body shape
   ____ facial features
   ____ mature appearance
   ____ personality
   ____ intelligence
2. Now rank the list by how important you think each quality is to *other* people's attractiveness. How do your two rankings differ?
3. Now reflect. Do you think that your rankings for yourself and others are as they *should* be? Explain. **WRITING**

2

GO ONLINE
PearsonSuccessNet.com
For resources and activities for this chapter.

Sensitive Issues

Students may be shy about sharing their thoughts on the subject of sexuality.
- It is possible to provide opportunities for student participation in nonthreatening ways through the use of examples to draw out student ideas or attitudes about gender roles and self-concept. For example, using role-plays can give students the opportunity to express their thoughts more anonymously.

Students often feel confused or embarrassed about sexual feelings.
- Explain that these are normal feelings and that everyone experiences them to some degree.
- Reassure students that everyone follows his or her own schedule of development, and has a different comfort level about expressing sexuality and discussing issues of sexuality.

3

VIDEO 20 TEENS Talk

Pictures of "Perfection"

Video Objectives

Use this video to help students

Identify some of the reasons why teens have a negative body image.

Analyze why media images of "perfect" bodies are not realistic.

Apply some techniques to become more accepting of their own bodies.

Preview **Activity**

What's Important to You?

Assign the Preview Activity for homework a few days before you plan to show the video. After students complete the activity, discuss how their rankings for "self" differed from their rankings for "others." You may also want to compile the rankings for the class and compare the class averages. Ask students if their rankings for "self" and "others" seem fair. After the discussion, ask students if they would change any of their rankings, and why.

From the Authors

Welcome to the subject in the high school curriculum that is, at once, both the easiest and most difficult to teach. It is the easiest because you will never have to motivate your students to read, discuss, or study the subject. Sexuality, in one form or another, has already gotten their attention. It is on their TVs, in their music, a part of their interaction with friends, and hopefully, a topic at their dinner table. Your students will find the subject interesting, and very timely. At the same time, however, teaching about sexuality is the most difficult assignment you may ever experience. It requires that you prepare much more than for other subjects. You will need to understand all district guidelines, be respectful of community concerns, and make parents feel like welcome partners in their children's sexuality education. Above all, you will need to respect your student's individuality and privacy. This is an important subject to teach. Enjoy it! And, good luck!

ABILITY LEVELS
L1 For students with special needs
L2 For less proficient readers
L3 For all students
L4 For gifted and talented students
EL For English language learners

Section 1

What Is Sexuality?

Objectives
Before class begins, write the objectives on the board. Have students copy the objectives into their notebooks at the start of class.

1. Focus

Warm-Up Myth/Fact

After students do the writing assignment, ask students to share their responses. Because of the very personal nature of the exercise, pass around a submission box so students can submit their responses anonymously. What did they think are some other common misunderstandings about sexuality? What answers do they hope the book will provide? Read aloud some of the responses to spark a class discussion.

2. Teach

Defining Sexuality

L2 Building Vocabulary
Put students in groups and have half the groups brainstorm a definition of *sexuality*. Have the other half brainstorm a definition of *gender*. Ask that each group include everyday examples that illustrate their definition. Ask for a volunteer from each group to read the definition and examples aloud.

Section 1

What Is Sexuality?

Objectives

- ▶ **Identify** how sexuality influences your personality and behavior.
- ▶ **Summarize** two areas of development significant to sexuality during the teen years.
- ▶ **List** four factors that influence sexuality.
- ▶ **Describe** how sexuality is expressed in everyday life.

Vocabulary

- **sexuality**
- **gender**
- **gender role**

Warm-Up

Myth **I don't need to know about sexuality since I'm not sexually active.**

Fact **Sexuality is an integral part of who you are and how you behave, regardless of sexual experience.**

WRITING What other myths do you think teens have about sexuality? What answers to the questions you have about sexuality do you hope this book will provide?

Defining Sexuality

As a teen, you are growing—physically, emotionally, mentally, socially, and creatively. And you are becoming more aware of your **sexuality**—everything about you that relates to, reflects, or expresses maleness or femaleness. Sexuality is influenced in large part by your sex—that is, being male or female in the biological sense. It is also influenced by your concepts of gender. **Gender** refers to the way people perceive maleness and femaleness to be defined by society.

Your sexuality influences how you think, how you feel about yourself and others, and how you behave. Remember that you do not need a boyfriend or girlfriend, nor to be sexually active, to express your sexuality. The way you dress and move, the gestures and facial expressions you use, the distance you stand from the person you are talking with, and other forms of body language convey your sexuality. What you say and how you say it can also reflect your sexuality. Talking comfortably about your body and your feelings, for example, is a positive expression of sexuality.

As a teen, you will experience significant changes in your awareness and expression of your sexuality. These are normal developments, but they may cause you to worry about your appearance, your feelings, and your behavior. Learning about your sexuality will help you to deal with these changes in a more confident way.

TEENS *Are Asking . . .*

Q: If sexuality is supposed to be such a natural expression of who you are, why am I always being told that my choice of clothing is too revealing? Why can't I be who I am?

A: The way you dress can send powerful messages, some of which may not be what you intend. You may dress a certain way because you feel good about the way your body looks. Other people, however, may interpret your style as a signal that you want to be involved in sexual situations. Sometimes, teens who dress in certain ways may acquire unfounded reputations about their sexual experience. You must balance how you like to dress with some of the possible negative messages that your style may convey.

Factors Affecting Sexuality

Your sexuality develops and changes as you mature. **Four factors that influence sexuality are family, the media, peers, and adult role models.**

Influence of Family The development of your sexuality begins when you are an infant. The touch of your parents, the warmth of your mother's body, and the sights and sounds that you experience all contribute to your awareness of your body as an infant. As you grow older, your parents serve as your first models of sexuality. When parents express physical affection with a hug or a kiss, children learn how their bodies can be used to express feelings in positive, healthy ways.

Parents also influence a child's understanding of gender roles. **Gender roles** are the behaviors and attitudes that are socially accepted as either masculine or feminine. These roles often are defined differently in different cultures. In fact, over time, they can change significantly within a culture. In the United States, gender roles have become less rigid in the last few decades.

Through their words and actions, parents display certain attitudes about gender roles in the family and as members of a community. For example, parents may share in household tasks and show respect for each other's work. By doing this, they foster the attitude that every person is of equal value and deserves respect.

Connect to Your Life **Describe one influence on how you view gender roles.**

FIGURE 1 Gender roles are influenced by social interactions that begin soon after birth and continue throughout childhood.

Factors Affecting Sexuality

L3 Class Discussion

Ask students what they think the saying "boys will be boys" means. Use their responses to introduce the topic of gender roles. Ask students to identify ways that people learn about traditional masculine and feminine roles. Which traditional roles are they comfortable with? Which would they like to see change?

L4 Cultural Connection

Have students research gender roles in other cultures and compare them to gender roles in mainstream American culture. Also have students explore how their own cultural heritage has influenced the development of their sexuality. However, give them the option to keep that aspect of their research private.

Connect to Your Life *Sample answer:* I was always roughhousing with my older brothers growing up, which made me believe girls can be athletic and strong.

Differentiated Instruction

L2 Less Proficient Readers

Use the visuals in Figure 1 to help less proficient readers understand the concept of gender roles. Ask: **Which picture or pictures do you think goes against traditional gender roles or stereotypes? Why?** *(Students might say the girl playing with a truck goes against the stereotype that girls play with dolls.)* Ask: **What lesson might the members of the soccer team be learning with regard to gender roles?** *(that both girls and boys can be athletic and can work together)*

L3 Content Update GO ONLINE

Visit Pearson SuccessNet to access more information about building a healthy body image. Have students complete the Web activity.

L2 Building Media Literacy

Bring in or request that students bring in some magazine ads that play on a typical teen's anxieties or feelings of inadequacy. In small groups, have students discuss what inadequacy each ad centers around. How does the product promise to address this inadequacy? Do students believe the message? Also have students discuss what tactics the advertiser is using to sell the product (for example, attractive models, a bandwagon approach, or an appeal to the senses).

L3 Visual Learning: Figure 2

Caption Answer *Sample answer:* Certain song lyrics might encourage teens to engage in sexual activity.

Connect to Your Life Answers will vary.

GO ONLINE
PearsonSuccessNet.com
For: More on building a healthy body image

Influence of the Media Much of what you see, hear, and read in the media—television, music, movies, magazines, and newspapers—conveys messages about sexuality. These media messages may contradict what you have learned from your family. Keep in mind that the media try to entertain or sell things to their customers. To do this, they often use themes that appeal to people's anxieties, concerns, or hopes about their own sexuality. For example, many teenagers are self-conscious about their appearance. Advertisers may exploit these concerns by suggesting that people need to use their products or services to be sexually appealing.

To attract audiences, some television programs and movies deal with topics that involve sexual behavior. The serious risks of sexual behavior—such as unplanned pregnancy and sexually transmitted infections—are dealt with on some shows, but more often than not, they are ignored.

The lyrics of many pop songs also have a sexual theme. Unfortunately, some of these songs do not present a responsible message. For example, some songs treat women as objects or even glorify sexual violence.

Although you can receive negative messages and misinformation from the various media, you also can receive positive messages. For example, some movies, radio and television programs, and written articles inform you and increase your awareness and understanding of sexuality.

Connect to Your Life **Which pop artists do you think portray sexuality in a responsible way? Explain.**

FIGURE 2 Popular music presents many messages about sexuality. **Predicting** How do you think song lyrics might influence teen behavior?

Media Wise

TV and Sexual Messages

How do your favorite TV shows portray teens? Are the teen characters better dressed, more beautiful, and more sex-savvy than students at your school? What kinds of messages about sex and sexuality are these fictional teens sending?

Do the teens act in responsible ways?	Yes	No
Do the teens have serious discussions with adult role models about sex?	Yes	No
Are the negative consequences of teen sex portrayed realistically?	Yes	No
Do any of the characters who have been sexually active later choose to be abstinent?	Yes	No

"Yes" answers represent more responsible messages about teen sex than "No" answers.

Activity Watch three TV shows that feature teens. For each show, use the checklist to evaluate each show's message about teens and sex. How did the shows compare? Which had the healthiest message for its viewers? Summarize your findings in a short essay.

Influence of Peers Your peers also influence the development of your sexuality. For example, many teenagers find it comforting to have a close friend to talk with about their latest crush, or to ask for advice about fashion, hair styles, and personal care products. Friends who have a healthy attitude about their own sexuality help to shape positive attitudes about sexuality in others.

Some teens judge their own expressions of sexuality against their perceptions of peer "norms." Perceptions of peer norms—those behaviors teens think are typically practiced by their peers—may not lead to healthy decisions. For example, some teens think that most of their peers are sexually active. Even though this perception is usually inaccurate, teens may feel pressure to become sexually active themselves, before they are ready.

Influence of Adult Role Models When you require reliable information about sexuality, to whom do you turn? In addition to talking to your parents, you may consult other family members, teachers, health professionals, clergy members, or other responsible adults. Even among well-informed adults, however, opinions about certain aspects of sexuality may vary greatly. It will be up to you to sort through the information you receive and to act responsibly.

Media Wise

TV and Sexual Messages

As a homework assignment for the week, ask students to watch three TV shows that feature teens (teen dramas), using the checklist to evaluate each one. Ask them to jot down examples from the show that illustrate each of their "Yes" or "No" responses. Have students discuss their findings in class. To get more involvement and interest in the class discussion, you may wish to have the students agree beforehand on three shows that everyone will watch so that they can better compare their answers. They may also want to draw on past episodes of the show to add to their examples.

Activity After the class discussion, have students write their short essays explaining which TV show they think contains the healthiest messages about teens and sex. Ask for volunteers to present one-sentence summaries of their essays to the class.

L3 Building Health Skills

Analyzing Influences Have students consider the following scenario: High-school sophomore Hannah is on a double date with her older sister, her sister's college boyfriend, and his roommate. Hannah's date is four years older than she is. Have the class discuss how the peer pressure on Hannah might be different in this situation than in one where she is out with people her own age.

WRITING and Health

L3 Editorial

Have each student write a letter to the editor of a local paper voicing their opinion about restricting teens' ability to purchase music containing sexually demeaning or violent lyrics. Have students support their view with points that are related to personal or social health. For example, one student might argue that singing and listening to lyrics that describe socially unacceptable viewpoints is a safe outlet for sexual fantasies (instead of actually acting on them). Another student might argue that explicit lyrics promote socially unacceptable behavior to impressionable teens.

Expressing Sexuality

L3 Cooperative Learning

Divide students into small groups of four or five and have them write the dialogue for a role-play that explores different opinions on how school uniforms affect (or not affect) teen expressions of sexuality. The roles played may be students, teachers, administrators, parents, or other community members. After they write their dialogues, have one or more groups present their role-plays to the class. Use the presentations to generate class discussion about whether or not school uniforms are a good idea.

3. Assess

Evaluate

These assignments can help you assess students' mastery of the section content.

L3 Section 1 Review

Answers appear below.

L2 Reteach

Have students create a concept map with the word *Sexuality* in an oval at the center. Have them summarize ideas from the section on their map and show how they are related to the central concept.

L4 Enrich

Health and Community

Media Messages Have students share their collages of magazine ads and their written summaries. Ask them what they think accounts for the similarities or differences in opinion between teens and adults, and between males and females.

FIGURE 3 By sitting close and sharing a joke, these teens are expressing their sexuality without even thinking about it.

Expressing Sexuality

Because sexuality is part of your personality, it is expressed in many of the things you do. The typical, everyday expressions of sexuality through dress, body language, and conversation usually happen on a subconscious level. Since they are so much a part of you, you tend not to think about them.

While you do not need to hide your sexual development, you do need to realize that calling attention to it with clothing or behavior may encourage situations you are not ready for. Similarly, you should not pretend an interest in someone if you do not feel it, and you should not be ashamed of these feelings if you have them.

Expressing sexuality to someone you consider special, on the other hand, involves a conscious effort to show your attraction and affection for that person. Sitting close, holding hands, and showing concern are all ways of expressing attraction and affection.

Often, two people in a relationship have different ideas about how they want to express their sexuality in a physical sense. They may disagree about how intimate they want to become. They may even feel different ways at different times. Whatever your feelings, you never owe anyone a more intimate sexual expression than you are comfortable with. You also should not pressure others to go farther in expressing their sexuality than is comfortable for them.

Section 1 Review

Key Ideas and Vocabulary

1. What is **sexuality?** How is it different from sexual activity?
2. What are **gender roles?**
3. How does sexuality change during the teen years?
4. List four factors that influence individual concepts of sexuality.
5. Give three examples of everyday expressions of sexuality.

Critical Thinking

6. **Applying Concepts** Give an example of one factor at your school that influences gender roles.
7. **Making Judgments** How do you think the factor you named in Question 6 affects students' concepts of sexuality? Explain.
8. **Relating Cause and Effect** Many teens think that more of their peers are sexually active than actually are. What are some of the reasons that teens might think this?

Health and Community

Media Messages Choose two or three magazine pictures that you think present messages about sexuality. Attach them to a sheet of paper and ask several teens and adults of both sexes to describe the sexual messages. Summarize their views. How do their views compare with your original views? WRITING

Section 1 Review

1. *Sample answer:* Sexuality is everything about a person that relates to, reflects, or expresses maleness or femaleness. Sexual activity is just one kind of expression of sexuality, but there are many other ways it is expressed, too.
2. Gender roles are the behaviors and attitudes that are socially accepted as either masculine or feminine.
3. *Sample answer:* During the teen years, there are significant changes in awareness and expression of sexuality.
4. Family, the media, peers, and role models
5. *Sample answer:* wearing a nice outfit, sitting close to someone, sharing a laugh
6. *Sample answer:* There are only boys in the science club.
7. *Sample answer:* This might make girls think they can't excel at science.
8. *Sample answer:* Lots of teens probably exaggerate their sexual experience because they think it will make them more popular.

Concerns of Adolescence

Section 2

Objectives
- ▶ **Identify** the physical changes related to sexuality that occur during puberty.
- ▶ **List** three factors that affect self-concept during adolescence.

Vocabulary
- adolescence
- puberty
- reproductive maturity
- secondary sex characteristics
- self-concept
- body image
- sexual awakening
- heterosexual
- homosexual
- bisexual

Warm-Up

Dear Advice Line,

I'm very self-conscious because I look more grown up than all of my friends. I'm tired of people staring at me and making comments about my body. What can I do?

WRITING What advice and reassurances would you offer this teen?

Changes in Your Body

If you were to compare a recent photograph of yourself to one taken three years ago, you would notice many changes. From about the ages of 12 to 19, you gradually change from a child into an adult. This period of gradual change is called **adolescence.** During adolescence, a person experiences many physical, mental, and emotional changes.

As photographs reveal, adolescence is a period of rapid physical growth. However, photos show only some of the changes taking place in your body. Important changes related to your sexuality are also happening. **During adolescence, the reproductive system matures and adult features appear. The timing of these changes varies greatly from person to person.**

The period of sexual development when a person becomes sexually mature and able to reproduce is known as **puberty.** Puberty usually begins before you reach adolescence and ends during mid-adolescence. You may have heard the term *puberty* used in many different ways. Some people use the term to refer to all of the changes of adolescence. However, the term refers specifically to the changes that happen to your reproductive system.

Section 2

Concerns of Adolescence

Objectives
Before class begins, write the objectives on the board. Have students copy the objectives into their notebooks at the start of class.

1. Focus

Warm-Up Advice

After students have completed their writing, ask volunteers to share their responses with the class. Then explain that the changes of adolescence often bring stress. Tell students that learning about the physical, emotional, and social changes that occur during adolescence can help reduce this stress.

2. Teach

Changes in Your Body

L3 Building Health Skills

Accessing Information Point out that the physical changes of puberty can be stressful and confusing. Have students identify possible sources of information about puberty (for example, the Internet, books, friends, school nurse, parents or guardians). Record their responses on the board. Then, review the list and have students explain how they would assess the reliability of each source of information.

Sensitive Issues

Students may feel uncomfortable discussing the changes of adolescence. Take steps to create a classroom environment in which students are encouraged, but not required, to join classroom discussions of these sensitive topics. Remind students that showing respect to others is particularly important during these discussions.

WRITING and Health

L3 Comparison

Ask students to write a paragraph that compares and contrasts puberty and adolescence. Encourage students to use a graphic organizer, such as a Venn diagram, to organize their thoughts before they write. Remind students that a paragraph should include a topic sentence and supporting details. After students have completed their writing, ask volunteers to share their paragraphs with the class. Use the students' writing to reinforce the correct usage of the terms *puberty* and *adolescence*.

L2 Visual Learning: Figure 4

Have students examine Figure 4, which describes the secondary sex characteristics that develop during puberty. Ask: **Why are the changes described in the figure classified as secondary sex characteristics?** *(These changes are not directly related to reproduction.)* Point out that the text mentions that these changes can be overwhelming. Ask: **What other adjectives might be used to describe the emotional impact of these physical changes?** *(Sample answers: scary, confusing, exciting, frustrating)*

EL Building Vocabulary

Ask students to recall the definition of the word *hormone*. *(chemical substance produced by an endocrine gland)* Tell students that the word *hormone* comes from a Greek word meaning "to stir up." Ask students to give examples of ways in which hormones can "stir up" one's life. *(Hormones stir up changes in physical appearance, leading to feelings of awkwardness and uncertainty.)*

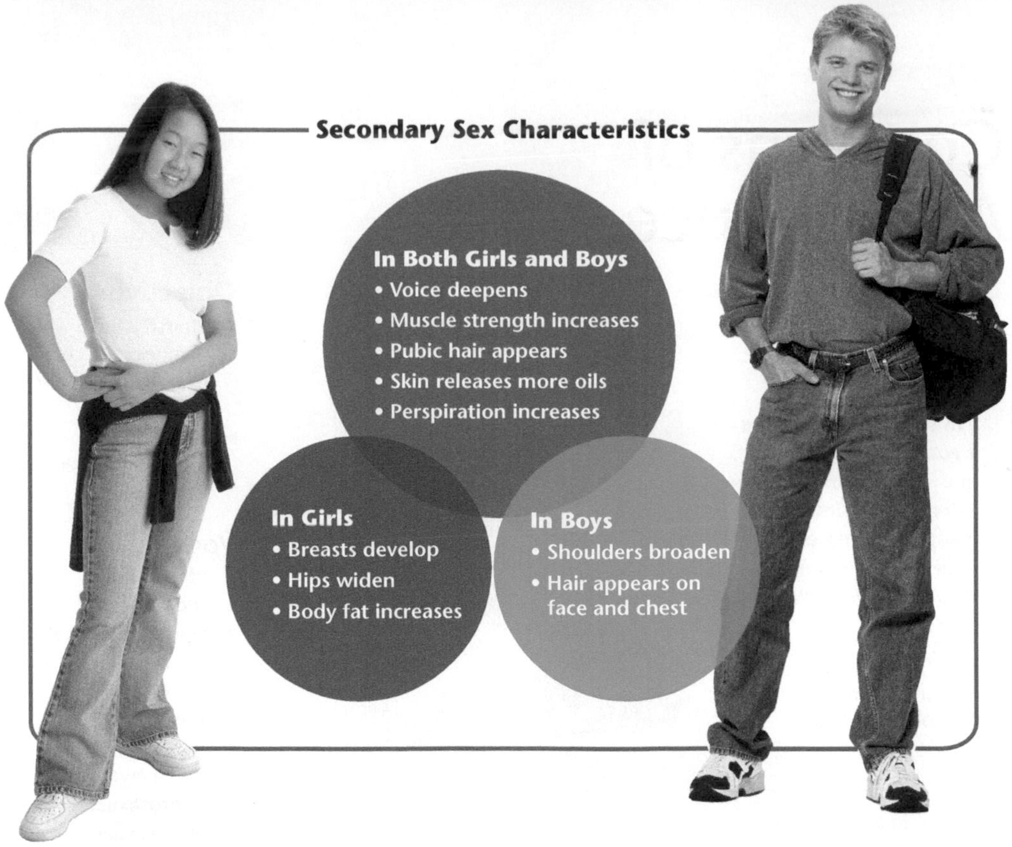

FIGURE 4 At puberty, sex hormones cause the development of secondary sex characteristics.

Reproductive System Sex hormones released from endocrine glands control the changes that occur during puberty. At some point between the ages of 9 and 16, the pituitary gland in the brain signals a girl's ovaries or a boy's testes to begin producing sex hormones. The ovaries produce eggs and the hormones estrogen and progesterone. The testes produce sperm and the hormone testosterone. You will learn more about the male and female reproductive systems in Chapter 2.

The release of sex hormones causes girls to begin to ovulate—to release eggs—and to menstruate. It causes boys to begin to produce sperm. Ovulation in girls and sperm production in boys signal **reproductive maturity,** or the ability to produce children.

Early in puberty, the body does not produce sex hormones consistently. In girls, this affects the regularity of the menstrual cycle. Many girls begin to ovulate before their menstrual cycles become regular. In fact, in some girls, menstrual cycles do not become regular for many years.

Appearance The sex hormones also cause the development of **secondary sex characteristics,** which are physical changes that develop during puberty, but are not directly involved in reproduction. Secondary sex characteristics are listed in Figure 4.

For Your INFORMATION!

Early Puberty

Some children reach puberty earlier than what is considered "normal." This is called precocious puberty. Precocious puberty is defined as showing signs of puberty before age 8 in girls or 9 1/2 in boys. Girls are more likely than boys to undergo precocious puberty.

It has been observed that more girls undergo precocious puberty today than a generation ago. The reasons for this phenomenon are unclear. Some studies have shown that obesity increases the chance that a girl will start puberty early. Other studies link precocious puberty to social factors or environmental pollution.

Some children require treatment for precocious puberty, which may include hormone therapy. Doctors and parents often are concerned about the negative emotional and social consequences of precocious puberty.

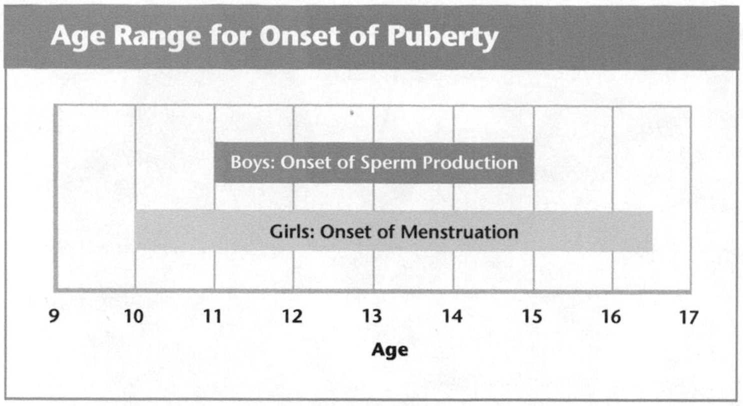

FIGURE 5 There is no "typical" age at which puberty begins. This timeline shows that the age range for onset of puberty is wide. **Calculating** What is the range in years between the earliest and latest onset of menstruation in girls? **MATH**

Early Bloomers and Late Bloomers If you are like most adolescents, you have probably compared your own physical development to that of your peers. Some of your classmates may already look like adults, while others may be just starting to show signs of puberty. You can see in Figure 5 that the age range for the "normal" onset of puberty is wide. Some people start puberty before middle school, some people start puberty toward the end of high school, and others start puberty somewhere in between.

Adolescents who develop at an early age, before most other adolescents, are sometimes called early bloomers. Those who develop at a later age, after most other adolescents, are called late bloomers. Although they may not think so, most early bloomers and late bloomers are developing at a normal rate.

What accounts for the wide range of ages at which puberty and the growth spurt begin? The ages at which people mature sexually and grow to their adult height are determined in large part by heredity. You are probably maturing at about the same age and speed as your parents did. Another factor that influences your unique timetable of development is your overall state of health.

Connect to Your Life **Do you consider yourself an early bloomer, late bloomer, or somewhere in between? Why?**

Adjusting to Change The physical changes at puberty can be overwhelming at times. Some adolescents have difficulty adjusting to their changing body shape, and some are embarrassed or confused about the sexual changes occurring to their bodies. Having someone to talk to, especially a trusted adult, can help adolescents understand the changes and accept their feelings.

GO ONLINE
PearsonSuccessNet.com
For: More on adolescence

L2 Visual Learning: Figure 5

Have students examine the graph that shows the age ranges for the onset of puberty. Ask: **Do boys or girls have a greater range of ages for onset of puberty?** *(girls)* **What are two factors that determine an individual's age of onset of puberty?** *(heredity and overall health)*

Caption Answer The range in age between the earliest and latest onset of menstruation in girls is 6.5 years.

L3 Building Health Skills

Communicating Read the following scenario to the class: Maria is smaller and less developed than the other girls in her gym class. She is so self-conscious about her body that she frequently leaves her gym clothes at home or cuts gym class. Have a class discussion of ways that good communication skills could help Maria resolve her problem in a healthy way. (For example, Maria could discuss her concerns about her development with her parents or explain her behavior to her physical education teacher.)

Connect to Your Life Allow students to answer this question in their private journals.

L3 Online Activity GO ONLINE

Visit Pearson SuccessNet to access more information about adolescence. Have students complete the Web activity.

Differentiated Instruction

EL English Language Learners

One of the challenges of learning a new language is mastering idioms and other non-literal meanings of everyday words. For example, students may be unfamiliar with the usage of *bloom* in "early bloomers" and "late bloomers." Allow students to work in pairs to use a dictionary to find out what *bloom* means in reference to plants (to flower) and to people (to mature). Ask each pair of students to share their answers. Extend the activity by discussing other figures of speech that use plant terminology (for example, to put down roots, to plant a seed of doubt, to branch out, to have a fruitful discussion).

Accepting Yourself

L3 Journal Writing

In their private journals, have students monitor their negative "self-talk." They should write down each negative thought they have about themselves during the course of one day. For example, some students might think their clothes are not as nice as what other students are wearing, or they might berate themselves for acting awkwardly around someone they are attracted to. Next to each negative thought, have students write a positive statement about themselves that disputes the negative self-talk. Assure students that they can keep their journal entries private. **WRITING**

L2 Class Discussion

Tell students that self-esteem tends to drop in both males and females around the beginning of adolescence. Ask: **Why do you think self-esteem tends to drop at the beginning of adolescence?** *(Sample answer: People start to compare their appearance or their accomplishments with others.)* Then, tell students that the self-esteem of females is generally lower than that of males. Ask: **Why do you think females tend to have lower self-esteem than males?** *(Sample answer: Many females may feel they are valued more for their physical appearance than for their other characteristics.)*

FIGURE 6 Developing a healthy self-concept means accepting yourself and being comfortable around others.

Accepting Yourself

Although puberty may bring physical changes before you feel prepared for them, it is a normal process that every teen experiences. Adjusting to these changes will affect your **self-concept**—that is, what you think of yourself, physically and mentally. Your self-concept will change during adolescence and continue to develop into adulthood. **Three factors that affect your self-concept are body image, emotions, and sexual feelings.**

Body Image The way you see your physical self, your **body image,** is an important part of your self-concept. Some changes you now see may please you, and you may emphasize them with clothing, make-up, or regular workouts at the gym. Other changes may cause you some grief, and you may try to hide or change them. If you are unhappy with your body image, try to focus on your strengths and appreciate your unique physical appearance.

Emotions The hormones that influence the physical changes of puberty also affect emotions. Changing levels of these hormones may create mood swings that can range from feelings of high energy and joy to feelings of exhaustion and depression. Flashes of anger, often for no apparent reason, are typical of the mood changes that accompany puberty. So is feeling "both ways at once"—for example, when you look forward to, yet dread, a school dance or simultaneously love and hate a parent or sibling.

The strong and sometimes conflicting emotions of adolescence can be confusing and stressful. It may help to ease your anxieties if you realize that everyone experiences these same problems to some degree during the natural process of becoming an adult.

12 *Chapter 1*

Sensitive Issues

Students need to hear that poor body image and low self-esteem are common problems among adolescents. Their concerns often are exacerbated by feelings of social ineptness. Urge students to focus on their positive qualities rather than their negative ones.

TEENS *Are Asking . . .*

Q: My friends are good-looking and athletic, but they seem to spend most of their time making mean comments about other kids who aren't as good-looking or athletic. Their comments make me feel uncomfortable. What is going on here?

A: It sounds as if your friends may not have as positive a body image as they actually should. The physical, emotional, and mental changes of adolescence can make teens unsure of themselves. Some people respond to this uneasiness by pointing out what is wrong with others. This could be why your friends are behaving this way. You might try discussing your feelings with them. Let them know that you feel uncomfortable with what they are doing. If they are not willing to change, you may have to decide whether or not you want to continue your friendship.

Sexual Awakening Many of the concerns about body image and emotions that teenagers experience are related to another aspect of puberty—an increased awareness of, and sexual attraction to, other people. These feelings of sexual attraction are sometimes referred to as **sexual awakening.** It is only natural that you want to appear physically attractive to people to whom you are sexually attracted.

Your first feelings of sexual attraction may involve someone you have always known but now like in a different way. Or, you may find yourself attracted to someone new, or to your fantasy of the perfect date or ideal mate. Sometimes it may seem as though you are sexually attracted to everyone or as though you will never be interested in anyone. Just as the rate of physical development varies from person to person, so does the age at which teenagers experience sexual awakening.

Sexual Orientation As people mature sexually, they begin to establish their sexual orientation, or sexual preference. Most people are **heterosexual** (het uh roh SEK shoo ul)—as adults they are attracted to people of the opposite sex. Some people are **homosexual** (hoh moh SEK shoo ul)—as adults they are attracted to members of their own sex. Adults who are attracted to members of both sexes are called **bisexual.**

It is not unusual for young adolescents to prefer friends of their own sex, to have same-sex crushes on older friends, or even to have some sexual attraction to members of their own sex. This does not mean that they are or will be homosexual or bisexual. In many cases, this is just a part of the process of working through and establishing sexual orientation. Whatever a person's sexual orientation, it is a natural part of his or her own sexuality. It is not known what factors ultimately determine a person's sexual orientation.

Section 2 Review

Key Ideas and Vocabulary

1. What are two kinds of physical change at puberty that relate to sexuality?
2. List two **secondary sex characteristics** that develop in both boys and girls during adolescence.
3. What are three factors that affect self-concept during adolescence?
4. What is **sexual awakening?**

Critical Thinking

5. **Comparing and Contrasting** What event signals reproductive maturity in females? In males?
6. **Making Judgments** Do you think it is more difficult to be an early bloomer or a late bloomer? Why?
7. **Applying Concepts** How can having a healthy body image help a person accept the changes of adolescence? Explain.

Health at Home

Self-Concept Evaluation Write down three things you like about yourself, three things you do routinely that you feel good about, and three tasks that were difficult for you to do but that you accomplished. Explain why each thing is important to your self-concept.

L1 Active Learning

Ask students to bring in a magazine photo that they think represents an important emotional aspect of adolescence. Have each student present his or her photograph and describe what emotional aspect of adolescence it illustrates. List each idea on the board. Have students use the ideas on the board to develop a description of emotional changes that accompany adolescence.

3. Assess

Evaluate

These assignments can help you assess students' mastery of the section content.

L3 Section 2 Review

Answers appear below.

L2 Reteach

Have student pairs organize the section's content into a chart or graphic organizer. Provide several completed graphic organizers for students to use as models. Circulate among the students to correct any errors or omissions. Remind students that their graphic organizers can be used as study aids.

L4 Enrich

Health at Home

Self-Concept Evaluation Encourage students to list positive mental and emotional characteristics as well as positive physical characteristics and accomplishments. Assure students that they will be allowed to keep their evaluations private.

Section 2 Review

1. The reproductive system matures, and adult features appear.
2. *Any two:* voice deepens, muscle strength increases, pubic hair appears, skin releases more oils, perspiration increases
3. body image, emotions, and sexual feelings
4. the increased awareness of, and sexual attraction to, other people
5. Ovulation; sperm production
6. Answers will vary. *Sample answer:* It is more difficult to be a late bloomer because it is embarrassing to feel like a kid while all your friends look like adults.
7. *Sample answer:* A healthy body image can contribute to your self-confidence as you adjust to the development of secondary sex characteristics.

Values and Responsibilities

Objectives
Before class begins, write the objectives on the board. Have students copy the objectives into their notebooks at the start of class.

1. Focus

Warm-Up Quick Quiz

Assure students that their journal entries will remain private. After students have completed the writing assignment, ask volunteers to explain reasons why teens' actions may not always be consistent with their values.

Connect to Your Life Allow students to answer this question in their private journals.

Section 3

Values and Responsibilities

Objectives

- **Identify** some of the serious consequences of sexual activity during adolescence.
- **Evaluate** how respecting individual differences and opinions can strengthen your self-concept.

Vocabulary

- value

Warm-Up

Quick Quiz In your private journal, rank the following values in order of their importance to you, from 1 (most important) to a 4 (least important). If two things seem of equal importance, you can give them the same number.

____ My health

____ My family's respect

____ Self-respect

____ Acceptance by my peers

WRITING How might your values affect your decisions about sexual activity? Are your actions consistent with your values? Would you like to re-examine either your decisions or your values? Explain.

What Are Your Values?

Greater freedom, greater independence, and greater responsibility—these are some of the things to expect during adolescence. But it's not always easy. While at times your parents may expect you to behave like an adult, at other times, you may feel they still treat you like a child. Sometimes, you may be furious about not being allowed to decide things for yourself. At other times, you may want someone to make the hard decisions for you.

Fortunately, as your world expands during adolescence, so does your ability to deal with it. You are learning to think ahead and to plan, to put yourself in someone else's place, to analyze, to predict consequences, and to see the many sides of an issue. With this new emotional and intellectual maturity, you become aware of your values. **Values** are the standards and beliefs that you consider important and that help you decide what is right and wrong. You have learned many of your values from your parents, guardians, other adults, religion, culture, and certain life experiences. Whatever your values, they act as guidelines for the decisions you are facing now and will face in the future.

Connect to Your Life **What people or experiences do you think have influenced your values the most?**

Sensitive Issues

Keep in mind that an individual's values are usually a product of their family and culture. Some students may not feel comfortable sharing values that they think differ from the values of others in the class. When discussing values, call on only students who volunteer.

Differentiated Instruction

EL English Language Learners

Divide the class into small groups that include both English language learners and fluent speakers. Have students make a list of thinking abilities that develop during adolescence. Many of these abilities, including learning to think ahead and predicting consequences, are discussed on this page.

Several of the words used to describe the abilities, such as *analyze* and *predict,* are important vocabulary for students to master. Have the students in each group work together to come up with one real or hypothetical example of each of these abilities.

Values and Sexual Decision-Making When facing an important decision, it is wise to examine your feelings and wishes in light of your values. Among the many decisions you may make in adolescence and as an adult are those involving the expression of your sexuality. The strong feelings that accompany your sexual development in adolescence are likely to lead to relationships that are based on mutual sexual attraction. The quiz at the beginning of this section helped you to identify how your values will affect your decision-making in such relationships. For example, suppose you value your family's respect the most, and they disapprove of sex before marriage. This knowledge will help you stick to your decision to be abstinent.

When sexual feelings are strong, it may be difficult to abstain from sexual activity, but it is well worth it. **Sexual activity can have serious consequences, including sexually transmitted infections and HIV, pregnancy, and negative effects on your relationships and self-esteem.** You will learn more about sexual decision-making and about skills for practicing sexual abstinence in Chapter 3.

Talking Things Over Making decisions about relationships and sexual activity can be difficult, even when you feel quite sure of your values. Sometimes, it is helpful to talk things over with a responsible adult just to get another perspective on a difficult situation. Try to begin your discussion with your parents, even if you are embarrassed. Their concern for you often can help you overcome embarrassment, disappointment, disagreements, or even anger. Additional help may be available from teachers, health professionals, members of the clergy, and counselors. It is not shameful to ask for guidance. To know you need help and to ask for and accept it is a sign of maturity.

FIGURE 7 Talking to a parent about sexual matters may be difficult, but can help you clarify your values and make good decisions.

2. Teach

What Are Your Values?

L3 Journal Writing

Provide students with several examples of statements that describe personal beliefs, such as "I believe all people should be treated with respect." In their private journals, ask students to write three "I believe . . ." statements that describe personal values related to parental relationships, friendships, or intimate relationships. They should also describe how they demonstrate each of these values to others. **WRITING**

L1 Visual Learning: Figure 7

In their private journals, have students make a list of adults they can talk to about relationships and sexual decisions. Students should also write down the questions they would like to ask, or questions that they have asked in the past.

TEENS *Are Asking . . .*

Q: My parents and I used to have a good relationship, but since I started dating, they don't trust me at all. What can I do to improve things between us?

A: Your dating may be difficult for your parents to handle because they can no longer protect you in the same way they did when you were younger. You should discuss the situation with your parents and give them an opportunity to air their concerns. Maybe you and your parents can establish some guidelines so that they will feel more comfortable. Take this time to reassure your parents that you share common values about relationships. Perhaps as they see you acting responsibly, they will return to their former trusting ways.

Chapter 1, Section 3

Appreciating Differences

L3 Active Learning

Distribute one index card to each student. On the card, have students describe one unique trait about themselves that they are proud of. Collect the cards and redistribute them randomly to the students (so that no one knows whose card they are holding). Have students read the cards aloud. Give students time to write about at least three new things they learned about their classmates. **WRITING**

3. Assess

Evaluate

These assignments can help you assess students' mastery of the section content.

L3 Section 3 Review

Answers appear below.

L2 Reteach

Write the word *values* on the board. Help students create a concept map about values based on the content in the chapter. Direct students to copy the map into their notebook so that they can use it for a study tool.

L4 Enrich

Health at School

Promoting Respect Student groups could begin their work by developing their own definition of "respect." Tell students that it might be beneficial for their posters to illustrate that respecting others can help a person improve his or her own self-concept.

FIGURE 8 By accepting your individuality and that of others, the pressure to conform to what you perceive as "normal" will ease.

Appreciating Differences

You know, of course, that everyone, including yourself, is different from everyone else. Everyone has his or her unique physical, mental, and sexual traits. Everyone has a unique personality. During adolescence, these differences often become more pronounced. At the same time, the pressure to conform—to be like everyone else—is especially strong. No one wants to seem particularly different. If, however, you accept your individuality and that of others, this pressure to conform eases.

Trying to see things from other people's points of view can strengthen your own self-concept. This means trying to be open to others' opinions. It means respecting each person's right to be what they are, even if you happen to be something quite different. It also means not pressuring people to go against their values just to be a part of your crowd. Accepting others will help you be comfortable with the ways you feel different from your peers. And it will help you feel more confident in making the decisions that are best for you.

Section 3 Review

Key Ideas and Vocabulary

1. What are **values?** Name three factors that can influence a person's values.
2. List three risks of sexual activity.
3. Explain how an appreciation of other points of view can strengthen self-concept.

Critical Thinking

4. Making Judgments Why are values important?
5. Applying Concepts How are values and sexual decision-making related?

Health at School

Promoting Respect Work with a small group of your classmates to produce a poster that promotes respect for all students. Arrange with your teacher to display your poster in a school hallway or assembly room.

Section 3 Review

1. Values are the standards and beliefs that you consider important and that help you decide what is right and wrong. *Any three:* parents, guardians, other adults, religion, culture, and certain life experiences.
2. Three risk factors of sexual activity are sexually transmitted infections including HIV, unplanned pregnancy, and negative effects on relationships.
3. Accepting the differences of others will help you be more comfortable with the ways in which you feel different from others.
4. *Sample answer:* Values are important because they help you make decisions in healthy and consistent ways.
5. *Sample answer:* Evaluating your values is an important step in making decisions about sexuality.

Chapter 1 Review

VIDEO **TEENS Talk**
Pictures of "Perfection" How did the video change your perception of models? Of yourself?

Reviewing Key Ideas

Section 1

1. Sexuality is best described as
   a. behavior involving sexual activity.
   b. something that causes pregnancy.
   c. expressions of sexual attraction.
   d. expressions of maleness or femaleness.
2. Which of the following affects teens' concepts of sexuality?
   a. childhood experiences
   b. movies and TV
   c. friends
   d. all of the above
3. How are sexuality and sexual activity related?
4. What are some ways in which parents influence their children's sexuality?
5. **Critical Thinking** How do popular media influence teen sexuality? Do you think the media's influence has a mostly positive or mostly negative effect on teen sexuality? Explain.
6. **Critical Thinking** How do culturally defined gender roles affect expressions of sexuality? Explain using two examples.

Section 2

7. Puberty
   a. is all the changes of adolescence.
   b. lasts longer than adolescence.
   c. is controlled by sex hormones.
   d. is more stressful for boys than for girls.
8. Which of the following is a secondary sex characteristic?
   a. reproductive maturity
   b. sperm production
   c. increase in perspiration
   d. increase in height
9. How does puberty affect a person's sexuality?
10. Describe a typical "mood swing" that a teen might experience.
11. What is sexual orientation? Define three kinds of sexual orientation.
12. **Critical Thinking** How do you think ads for acne cures on TV affect teen body image? Explain.

Section 3

13. Beliefs that help you decide between right and wrong are called
   a. gender roles. **b.** opinions.
   c. values. **d.** self-concepts.
14. What values have you learned from your parents?
15. Why is it helpful to talk to a trusted adult about sex and sexuality?
16. **Critical Thinking** How would you describe to a young child what the term *values* means?

Building Health Skills

17. **Analyzing Influences** Your younger sister's friends are telling her to stop spending time at math club and start paying more attention to looking sexy. What is the message that she is getting about her sexuality? What advice would you give her? **WRITING**
18. **Advocacy** Your friend is wondering if he might be homosexual. Some of his old friends have started to avoid him and he is feeling depressed. How can you help? What other support would you recommend he seek out?
19. **Making Decisions** Suppose your "popular" friends spend a lot of their time making unkind comments about other teens who aren't part of their crowd. This makes you uncomfortable. What would you do?

Health and Community

Gender Roles In a small group, brainstorm a list of negative gender stereotypes that affect males and females. Discuss how these stereotypes limit both sexes from reaching their full potential. What gender stereotypes in your community would you like to see change? Write and perform a skit that shows what an "alternative" world without the stereotype would be like.

Chapter 1 Review

Reviewing Key Ideas

Section 1

1. d. **2.** d.

3. Sexual activity is just one form of expression of sexuality—it is not necessary to express one's sexuality.

4. *Sample answer:* Parents show physical affection to each other, which teaches children how to use their bodies to express feelings.

5–6. Answers will vary.

Section 2

7. c **8.** c

9. During puberty, a person matures sexually and develops secondary sex characteristics, which make a person more aware of his or her sexuality.

10. *Sample answer:* A teen might experience a flash of anger at a parent who he feels is being strict.

11. Sexual orientation is a person's sexual preference. Heterosexuals are attracted to members of the opposite sex. Homosexuals are attracted to members of their own sex. Bisexuals are attracted to both males and females.

12. Answers will vary. Some students may say the ads are good for teen body image because they show other teens who have struggled with acne. Other students may say the ads are bad because they show unrealistic results.

Section 3

13. c

14. Answers will vary. Student answers should indicate that they understand the meaning of the word *values.*

15. *Sample answer:* Because adults have had more life experiences with sex and sexuality, they are capable of giving sound advice.

16. Answers will vary.

Health and Community

Gender Roles Help groups stay focused on the task and serve as a mediator if group members disagree on which gender stereotypes are negative or should change.

Building Health Skills

17. *Sample answer:* This might be giving her the message that doing math is a male trait, and worrying about being beautiful is a female trait. I would advise her to be herself and know that challenging what some people consider to be traditional gender roles is fine, especially if those roles are limiting her personal growth.

18. *Sample answer:* I could help by listening if he wants to talk. I would recommend that he talk to a trusted adult or counselor about his feelings.

19. *Sample answer:* I would point out to my friends that everyone has a right to express themselves in unique ways. If they continued to make unkind comments, I would not participate in the conversations.

Chapter Preview

Section 1 The Male Reproductive System
Functions of the male reproductive system are to produce sex hormones, produce and store sperm, and deliver sperm to the female reproductive system. Caring for the system includes cleanliness, self-exams, and regular medical checkups.

Section 2 The Female Reproductive System
Functions of the female reproductive system are to produce sex hormones, produce eggs, and nourish a developing baby. Eggs are released during the menstrual cycle. Caring for the system includes cleanliness, self-exams, and regular medical checkups.

National Health Education Standards Correlation

1.12.4, 1.12.5, 2.12.5, 2.12.6, 3.12.1, 3.12.2, 3.12.4, 7.12.1, 7.12.2, 7.12.3, 8.12.2

Chapter 2

The Reproductive System

GO ONLINE PearsonSuccessNet.com

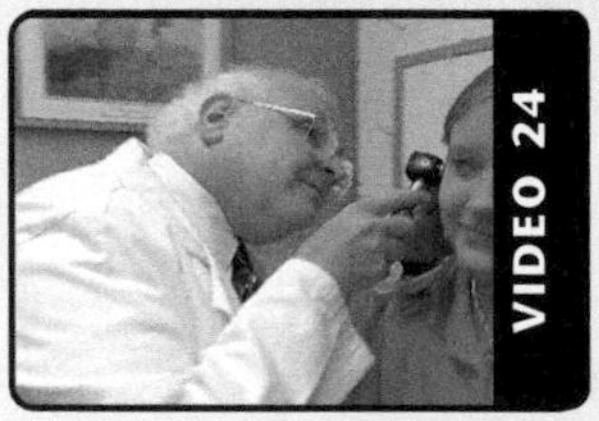

TEENS Talk

Taking Charge of Your Health

Preview **Activity**

Where Do You Get Your Health Information?

Complete this activity before you watch the video.

1. Choose a health topic you would like to know more about.
2. Write down a list of different sources that could provide you with more information on that topic. **WRITING**
3. Rank the sources you listed from most reliable to least reliable.
4. When you have looked for health information in the past, did you go to the most reliable source? Why or why not?

GO ONLINE
PearsonSuccessNet.com
For resources and activities for this chapter.

Sensitive Issues

- Reproduction is likely to be a sensitive issue for many students because of its association with sexual activity. Some students may hide their own sensitivity—or exploit that of others—by making crude comments or laughing inappropriately. Try to stem this behavior to make the issue less sensitive for other students.
- You should also be aware of cultural differences that might make the issue especially sensitive for some students. For example, students from certain cultural backgrounds may feel very uncomfortable discussing reproduction in class, because in their culture, adults do not typically talk to young people about issues related to sex.

19

VIDEO 24 **TEENS Talk**

Taking Charge of Your Health

Video Objectives

Use this video to help students

Understand the importance of getting regular medical checkups.

Identify reliable sources of health information.

Make responsible decisions regarding their own healthcare.

Preview **Activity**

Where Do You Get Your Health Information?

Before watching the video, have students complete the Preview Activity by writing their answers in their private journals. After showing all three portions of the video, ask students to revisit their list of sources and their reliability rankings. They should make a new list based on what they learned from the video.

From the Authors

Students may be more willing to discuss issues related to human reproduction and sexuality if they know appropriate terminology. One challenge in teaching these topics is the existence of multiple words to refer to structures of the male and female reproductive systems. The words include scientific terms, euphemisms learned in childhood, and slang words that are used "on the street."

This chapter is most appropriately taught using scientific terms. Discourage the use of euphemistic or "street" words by students. Encouraging the use of scientific terms will help students show respect for each other. It will also help them view the reproductive anatomy and processes more like they do other biological processes in the body.

ABILITY LEVELS

- **L1 For students with special needs**
- **L2 For less proficient readers**
- **L3 For all students**
- **L4 For gifted and talented students**
- **EL For English language learners**

Section 1

The Male Reproductive System

Objectives
Before class begins, write the objectives on the board. Have students copy the objectives into their notebooks at the start of class.

1. Focus

Warm-Up Myth/Fact

After students do the writing assignment, ask a few volunteers to share what they wrote. Some reasons you might discuss if the students don't bring them up include: family or cultural attitudes that discourage frank discussion of reproductive functions, embarrassment that keeps them from asking questions regarding "private" areas of their bodies, and false information given by peers and the media. Discuss how the myths could affect the health of teenagers.

Section 1

The Male Reproductive System

Objectives

- ▶ **Describe** three functions of the male reproductive system.
- ▶ **Identify** five ways to keep the male reproductive system healthy.

Vocabulary

- sperm
- fertilization
- testes
- testosterone
- scrotum
- penis
- semen
- ejaculation
- erection
- orgasm
- nocturnal emission
- masturbation
- testicular torsion
- infertility

Warm-Up

Myth **Cancers of the male reproductive system only affect older men.**

Fact **Cancer of the testis (testicular cancer) is most common in teens and young men, not older men.**

WRITING Why do you think that people have a number of misconceptions about the reproductive system?

Structure and Function

One essential function of all living things is reproduction, the process by which organisms produce offspring. In humans, the process begins with the development of reproductive cells in the bodies of males and females. In males, the reproductive cells are called **sperm.** **The functions of the male reproductive system are to produce sex hormones, to produce and store sperm, and to deliver sperm to the female reproductive system.** There, a sperm cell may join with an egg in a process called **fertilization.** Under the right conditions, a fertilized egg develops into a baby.

Testes Look at Figure 1 to see the organs of the male reproductive system. Locate the two oval-shaped **testes** (TES teez), the male reproductive glands. The testes (singular, *testis*) have two major functions—the production of testosterone and the production of sperm. The sex hormone **testosterone** affects the production of sperm and signals certain physical changes at puberty, such as the growth of facial hair.

The testes, also called testicles, hang outside the main body cavity, within a sac of skin called the **scrotum.** Because they are located outside the body, the temperature of the testes is a few degrees lower than the temperature inside the body. Sperm need this lower temperature to develop properly and survive.

In some males, one or both of the testes may not descend into the scrotum before birth, a condition called undescended testis. Sperm will not develop properly in an undescended testis because the temperature is too high. The condition is also a risk factor for testicular cancer. Surgery is usually performed before age two to correct this condition.

WRITING and Health

L3 Descriptive Writing
Have students describe male reproductive structures and their functions as though they are writing to inform an extraterrestrial alien—that is, someone who has no prior knowledge of human biology or reproduction. Students' descriptions should be clear, detailed, and complete, leaving nothing for readers to infer or imagine. This activity requires students to describe the male reproductive system so thoroughly that any gaps or misconceptions in their knowledge should be revealed to them as they write. Let students use their textbooks as needed to fill any gaps and correct any errors.

Penis The **penis** is the external sexual organ through which sperm leave the body. The tip of the penis is covered with loose skin, called the foreskin. In some males the foreskin is removed shortly after birth. This surgical procedure is known as circumcision. The decision to circumcise an infant is usually based on cultural or religious reasons. Whether there is an overall health benefit to circumcision is still being debated.

Other Structures Besides the external structures, the male reproductive system also includes internal ducts and accessory glands. These structures, which are shown in Figure 1, play an important role in storing and releasing sperm.

Sperm Production Once a male reaches puberty, millions of sperm are produced in his testes each day. Sperm production begins when the hypothalamus signals the pituitary gland to release two hormones—luteinizing hormone (LH) and follicle-stimulating hormone (FSH). LH signals the testes to begin making testosterone. Testosterone and FSH then trigger the production of sperm. Sperm production continues throughout adulthood.

Connect to Your Life **Why do you think some people are uncomfortable using the proper terms for reproductive structures?**

Male Reproductive System

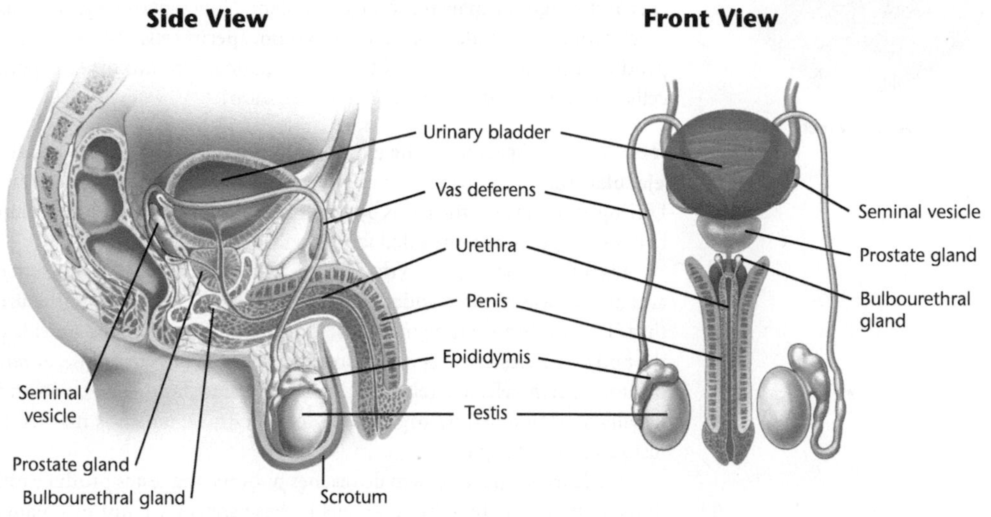

FIGURE 1 The male reproductive system produces, stores, and releases sperm.

2. Teach

Structure and Function

L2 Class Discussion

On the board, draw a flowchart entitled, "How Hormones Control Sperm Production." Draw three boxes labeled *Hypothalamus, Pituitary Gland,* and *Testis.* Remind students that the testis produces sperm. Draw an arrow from *Hypothalamus* to *Pituitary Gland,* and label it "Signal." Draw an arrow from *Pituitary Gland* to *Testis* and another from *Testis* back to itself. Ask students what hormones these two arrows represent. *(LH and FSH for the first arrow, testosterone for the second arrow)* Label the arrows, and call on students to describe the completed flowchart in their own words.

L3 Visual Learning: Figure 1

Image Bank Figure 18-3

Ask students to examine the figure and read the caption. Have them find the structures described in the text. *(testis, scrotum, penis)* Remind students that the urinary bladder and urethra store urine and carry urine out of the body, respectively. Explain that the urethra also carries semen out of the body. Challenge students to predict the roles of remaining structures before they read about them next. *(transporting, storing, and/or adding fluid to sperm)*

Connect to Your Life *Sample answer:* They are embarrassed to talk about the "private" parts of the body using proper terms, which are often unfamiliar and formal sounding. Using slang terms may be more comfortable because such terms are used more often by peers and in popular culture (in books, on T.V., etc.) than the proper terms.

Differentiated Instruction

L2 Less Proficient Readers

Show students how to organize information about the male reproductive system in a simple table on the board. Summarizing information in a table or other graphic organizer can help students see the main points without distracting details. Start the table with two columns headed *Structure* and *Function.* Under *Structure,* fill in the first column with the terms *Testis, Penis,* and other male reproductive structures. Have students find the functions of the structures in the text and read them aloud. Add the functions to the table. Urge students to use this kind of strategy whenever they become bogged down reading detailed passages.

L2 Visual Learning: Figure 2

Image Bank Figure 18-4

Pair students of the same gender, and have partners work together to create a flowchart of the pathway of sperm, as described in the figure. Flowcharts should show all the structures that sperm pass through or near and what happens to the sperm at each structure. *(Sperm are produced in the testes; mature in the epididymis; travel through the vas deferens; combine with fluids from the seminal vesicles, bulbourethral glands, and prostate gland; and leave the body through the urethra in the penis.)* Set aside class time for pairs to work on the activity. Display their flowcharts in the classroom.

Caption Answer in the epididymis

L1 Teacher Demo

Borrow from a biology teacher a microscope and slide showing human sperm. Set up the slide for viewing by students with special needs to help their understanding of sperm structure.

L3 Addressing Misconceptions

Sperm and Semen Students may have the misconception that semen contains only or mostly sperm. Explain that sperm cells are extremely tiny and contribute only a small amount to the total volume of semen. Instead, semen is made up mostly of fluids from the seminal vesicles, prostate gland, and bulbourethral glands. Ask: **Why are the fluids in semen important?** *(The fluids protect the sperm, provide them with energy, and help them pass through the urethra.)*

The Pathway of Sperm

FIGURE 2 Sperm travel through the reproductive system before they are released. **Interpreting Diagrams** Where do sperm complete their maturation?

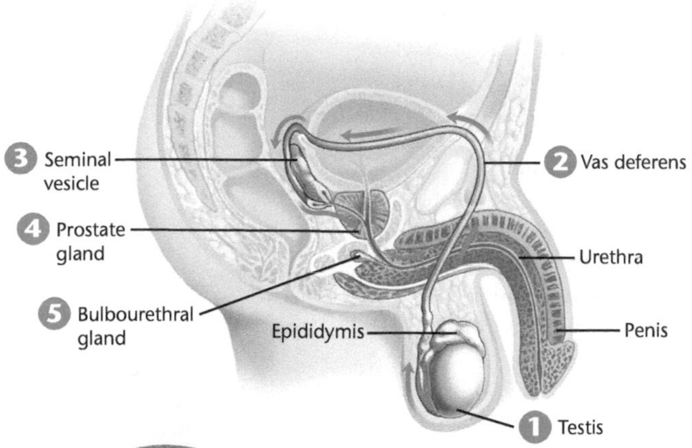

1. Sperm are produced in the **testes.** They mature and are stored in the **epididymis.**
2. Sperm travel through the **vas deferens** to the seminal vesicles.
3. **Seminal vesicles** add a fluid that provides a source of energy for the active sperm.
4. The **prostate gland** adds a fluid that protects the sperm.
5. The **bulbourethral glands** add a fluid that protects sperm from acidic conditions in the **urethra.**

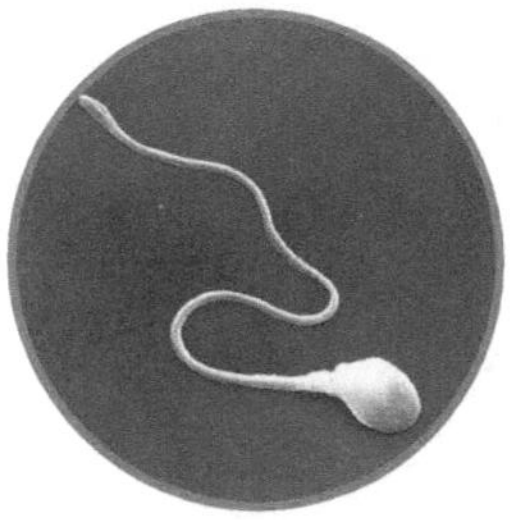

▲ **A sperm cell**

The Pathway of Sperm Look at Figure 2 to track the pathway of sperm through the male reproductive system. Note that during their passage through the male reproductive system, sperm cells mix with fluids produced by the prostate and two other glands. The mixture of sperm cells and these fluids is called **semen** (SEE mun).

Release of Sperm The ejection of semen from the penis is called **ejaculation.** Ejaculation occurs when the penis is in an erect state. During an **erection,** the penis becomes larger and stiffer as blood chambers in the penis become filled with blood.

Ejaculation occurs when the muscles in the male reproductive system and at the base of the bladder contract, forcing semen through the urethra. The urethra—a tube that passes through the penis to the outside of the body—carries urine as well as sperm, but not at the same time. Several million sperm cells are released during one ejaculation. Ejaculation is usually accompanied by **orgasm,** or sexual climax, which is marked by feelings of intense pleasure.

You learned that after a male reaches puberty, the testes produce millions of sperm daily. What happens if these sperm are not ejaculated? Sperm stored in the male reproductive system eventually degenerate, meaning they break down, and are disposed of.

For Your INFORMATION!

Sperm Facts

- Humans have some of the smallest sperm cells among mammals. For example, human sperm are much smaller than the sperm of rats or mice.
- Sperm remain alive inside the female reproductive tract for an average of 24 to 48 hours.
- Researchers recently discovered that the tails of sperm contain odor receptors. The receptors cause sperm to swim toward certain chemicals. Their ability to "smell" may explain how sperm can find their way to an egg through the maze of the female reproductive tract.

Concerns at Puberty

Most boys have many questions and concerns about the changes that occur to their bodies during puberty.

Sexual Arousal One change that results from the rise in hormone levels is an increase in sexual feelings. Males have erections throughout their lives, from babyhood to old age. At puberty, however, a male may have erections more frequently, sometimes for no apparent reason. Such erections may sometimes be embarrassing, but they are normal.

During puberty, males may also notice that they are more sensitive to sexual stimulation. Sexual fantasies, being close to an attractive person, touching the penis or scrotum, wearing tight clothing, and even needing to urinate can all cause an erection. An erection does not need to result in ejaculation—in fact, most do not. The penis soon returns to its soft state.

Nocturnal Emissions It is also common for a teen male to experience a **nocturnal emission,** or "wet dream," which is ejaculation during sleep. Nocturnal emissions occur because sperm production during puberty causes an increased pressure in the reproductive system. Nocturnal emissions are normal and may occur frequently. It is also normal not to experience nocturnal emissions.

Masturbation Orgasm and ejaculation can also result from masturbation. **Masturbation** is the touching of one's own genitals for sexual pleasure. Some people once thought that masturbation could cause acne, mental illness, infertility, and other bad effects. This is not true. However, some people today still object to masturbation on moral or religious grounds. Most doctors agree that masturbation is harmless unless it becomes a preoccupation, makes you feel guilty, or interferes with your daily activities.

Physical Appearance It is also common for teen males to be concerned about their physical appearance. Many teen males, for example, worry about the size of their penis. Size depends on heredity and on the stage of puberty the male has reached. The eventual size of the penis has nothing to do with a male's ability to reproduce or to give a partner sexual pleasure. Furthermore, most erect penises are about the same size, no matter how large or small they are when they are not erect.

Breast enlargement is another thing that worries some teen males during puberty. About 40 percent of boys have some breast swelling or tenderness, especially early in puberty when hormone levels change rapidly. This condition usually reverses itself as hormone production becomes more constant. Any teen male who is concerned about breast enlargement should consult his doctor.

FIGURE 3 Changes at puberty can lead to concerns about your physical appearance. Remember that not all boys experience puberty the same way, or at the same age.

Concerns at Puberty

L3 Journal Writing

Have the boys in your class write a private journal entry about any concerns they have about their changing bodies. Tell them that if any of their concerns are not addressed by what they read in the text, they can talk to their doctor. Have students use their journal entries to create a list of questions for the doctor. In most cases, the doctor will reassure them that what they are going through is perfectly normal. **WRITING**

Differentiated Instruction

L4 Gifted and Talented

There have been numerous scientific studies about how the environment affects human sexual development, particularly at puberty. Have interested students look up the results of a study about how a factor such as geography, socioeconomic status, or environmental chemicals has affected sexual development in people. Ask students to summarize what they learn in an oral report.

Keeping Healthy

L3 Content Update GO ONLINE

Visit Pearson SuccessNet to access more information about male reproductive health. Have students complete the Web activity.

L3 Building Media Literacy

Ask each student to bring to class a print media article on keeping the male reproductive system healthy. Students can use magazines, newspapers, or pamphlets. Ask several students to report on the relevance of their articles. Make sure several different types of print media are represented. Based on their reports, discuss whether certain types of print media seem more appropriate for this kind of information.

L2 Cooperative Learning

Ask students to work in groups to create brochures explaining how and why to care for the male reproductive system. Brochures should cover cleanliness, sexual abstinence, protection from trauma, self-exams, and regular medical checkups. Brochures should also describe health problems that can occur without good care of the male reproductive system. Suggest to students that they share their brochures with male family members or friends. **WRITING**

GO ONLINE
PearsonSuccessNet.com
For: More on male reproductive health

Keeping Healthy

A number of medical conditions can affect the male reproductive system. However, teens who adopt healthy habits can reduce their risk of problems. **Caring for the male reproductive system involves cleanliness, sexual abstinence, protection from trauma, self-exams, and regular medical checkups.**

Cleanliness Healthy habits start with cleanliness. It is important to thoroughly clean the external organs—the penis and scrotum—daily, preferably during a shower or bath. Each day, an uncircumcised male should gently pull the foreskin back to clean the head of the penis. Drying the groin area well after showering can prevent fungal infections that cause jock itch.

Sexual Abstinence A number of serious infections of the reproductive system and other body systems can result from sexual contact. Healthy choices regarding sexual behavior can prevent such infections. The only way to eliminate your risk of sexually transmitted infections is to abstain—or refrain from—sexual activity. In other words, practice sexual abstinence. Sexually transmitted infections will be discussed further in Chapter 5.

Protection From Trauma Good health also requires protection and prevention. During athletic activities, males should wear a protector, also called a "cup," or supporter. Tight clothing should be avoided, since tight pants or underwear can irritate or cause pain in the groin area.

Males should also be careful when lifting heavy objects. Pressure in the abdomen during lifting can push a loop of intestine out of the abdominal cavity, causing a hernia. An inguinal (ING gwuh nul) hernia results if part of the intestine pushes into the scrotum. Surgery is almost always necessary to correct an inguinal hernia.

One of the most serious reproductive disorders that may affect male teens is testicular torsion. **Testicular torsion** is the twisting of a testis so that the blood vessels leading to the testis also twist, cutting off the blood supply. Testicular torsion can happen during strenuous exercise or even during sleep.

Testicular torsion is a medical emergency. If you ever have sudden pain or swelling of a testis, you must see a doctor *immediately.* The blood vessel has to be untwisted by a surgeon within about six hours to keep the testis alive.

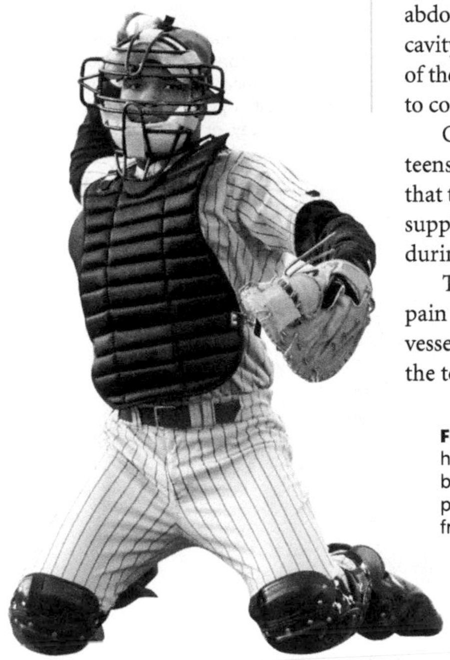

FIGURE 4 This catcher protects himself with a helmet, face guard, body padding, and a "cup" that protects his reproductive organs from injury.

TEENS *Are Asking . . .*

Q: Only athletes who are frequently in locker rooms get jock itch, right?

A: Although the name implies that only athletes get this infection, any male can get it. (It is less common in females.) Jock itch is a fungal infection of the skin. Moisture from water or sweat can allow the fungus to grow, which causes itching and sometimes burning. A red rash may also appear in the groin area and may spread down the inner thighs.

The best way to prevent jock itch is to wear loose-fitting clothing, avoid sharing towels, and dry the groin area thoroughly after showering or exercising. There are over-the-counter treatments for jock itch. However, if you are not sure that you have jock itch, if your symptoms don't clear up quickly, or if you have been engaging in sexual activity, you should make an appointment to see your doctor.

Self-Exams It is important for males to monitor their own bodies for any signs of possible medical problems. Pain when urinating, unusual discharges, or sores on the genitals require a medical examination. Such conditions should not be self-treated.

Males, especially teens and young men, should also examine their testes for signs of testicular cancer. Many testicular cancers occur in males in their teens and twenties. Testicular cancer is the most common type of cancer in males between 15 and 34 years of age. However, it can be cured if detected early and treated promptly. Most testicular cancers are first noticed by men themselves, not by their doctors.

Figure 5 outlines the procedure for the testicular self-exam. The best time to perform a self-exam is after a hot shower or bath, when the scrotum is relaxed and the testes can be felt more easily. The American Cancer Society recommends that teen males discuss with a doctor how often to perform self-exams.

Connect to Your Life **Why is it important for males in their teens to know the symptoms of testicular cancer?**

FIGURE 5 Males should follow this procedure to perform the testicular self-exam.
Comparing and Contrasting Where is the typical location of an abnormal lump compared with the location of the epididymis?

Testicular Self-Exam

1 Examine each testis separately with both hands.

- Roll each testis between the thumbs and fingers of both hands.
- Look and feel for any hard lumps or smooth, rounded masses, or any change in the size, shape, or texture of the testes. If lumps are present, they are usually found in the front or sides of the testes.
- Learn to recognize what the epididymis feels like so you won't confuse it with a lump. The epididymis appears as a small "bump" on the back side of the testis, toward the back of the body.

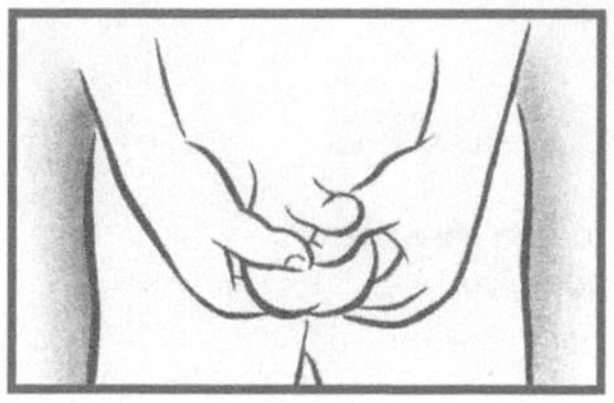

2 Report any abnormalities to your doctor immediately.

- Lumps may not be cancerous, but only a doctor can make a diagnosis.
- Other signs of testicular cancer are enlargement of a testis, dull aching in the genital area, or a feeling of heaviness in the scrotum. However, testicular cancer is not typically painful when it first develops.

L2 Visual Learning: Figure 5

Guide students through the steps of the self-exam. Have students create an index card that lists warning signs males should look for when performing a self-exam. Encourage male students to use the card when they perform the self-exam. Encourage female students to give the card to a male family member.
Caption Answer Abnormal lumps are usually found in the front or sides of the testes. The epididymis is found on the back side of the testis.

L3 Building Media Literacy

When a celebrity is affected by an illness, the media often take note. Give students the example of how Lance Armstrong brought attention to testicular cancer (for example, through promotion of the yellow "Livestrong" bracelets). Ask students to think of other examples of how celebrities have brought attention to various health issues. Ask: **Do the media do a good job of promoting healthful behaviors with regard to celebrities' illnesses?**

Connect to Your Life It is important because almost a third of testicular cancer cases occur in young men in their teens and twenties.

Differentiated Instruction

L1 Special Needs

Some doctors have models of testes with lumps. If possible, borrow a model and let male students examine the model to experience what a lump might feel like. Try to convince students of the importance of doing self-exams by citing the following statistic: In 2004 in the United States, about 9,000 new cases of testicular cancer were diagnosed, most of which were in teens and young men. Most of the tumors were noticed first by the patients themselves.

Sensitive Issues

Students may be uncomfortable discussing or asking questions about the testicular self-exam (or about the breast self exam discussed in Section 2 on page 35). Keep the discussion objective, and focus on the role of self-exams in detecting cancer early and saving lives. Suggest to students that they ask for a demonstration from a nurse or doctor the next time they have a medical appointment if they are uncertain how to do the self-exam correctly.

1. Assess

Evaluate

These assignments can help you assess students' mastery of the section content.

L3 Section 1 Review

Answers appear below.

L2 Reteach

List each of the section vocabulary terms on the board. Then point to each word and have students brainstorm facts about that term. Record the most important, accurate facts on the board. Do not move on to the next term until students can no longer think of additional facts. For any terms students know little about, have them reread relevant passages in the section. Suggest that students record the facts for each term in their notebooks.

L4 Enrich

Health at Home

Reminder Card E-mails will vary but should give persuasive reasons for regular medical checkups and self-exams. For example, students might stress the importance of self-exams in finding cancer early while it is still curable. Acting as advocates in this way may help persuade students to take good care of their own reproductive system.

FIGURE 6 Your doctor can answer any questions you have about your reproductive health.

Medical Checkups Medical exams throughout life can help ensure reproductive health. Teen males should expect a few differences in procedure from their childhood checkups. For example, the doctor will probably feel around your genitals to check for lumps or pain. The doctor may also ask you whether you have ejaculated, and whether you have any concerns about your sexual development. This is the time to bring up any worries you have or just to ask questions out of curiosity.

The prostate gland is of particular concern after middle age. In many older men, the prostate becomes enlarged or develops cancer. An enlarged prostate does not necessarily indicate either disease or illness, but it can cause discomfort and frequent urination. An enlarged prostate may also make urination painful or difficult. If that happens, surgery is usually required.

Starting at age 50, men are encouraged to get screened for prostate cancer during their regular medical exams. After lung cancer, prostate cancer is the second most common cause of cancer death in men.

Another condition a doctor can diagnose is **infertility,** the condition of being unable to reproduce. Infertility can affect both males and females. In males, infertility is marked by the inability to produce healthy sperm or the production of too few sperm. Three causes of infertility are exposure to certain chemicals, having mumps after puberty, and having an undescended testis.

Section 1 Review

Key Ideas and Vocabulary

1. What are three main functions of the male reproductive system?
2. What is the name of the sac in which the **testes** are located?
3. What is **semen**, and how is it formed?
4. List five things that males should do to maintain reproductive health.
5. What are two kinds of problems with sperm that can lead to **infertility** in males?

Health at Home

Reminder Card Write an e-mail to a male family member reminding him of the importance of regular medical checkups and self-exams. **WRITING**

Critical Thinking

6. **Sequencing** Arrange the following structures in the order in which sperm pass by or travel through them: epididymis; vas deferens; testes; prostate gland; seminal vesicles
7. **Applying Concepts** How could more young men be convinced to follow the recommendations for reproductive health? **WRITING**

Section 1 Review

1. to produce sex hormones, to produce and store sperm, and to deliver sperm to the female reproductive system
2. scrotum
3. Semen is a mixture of sperm cells and fluids. It forms when sperm from the testes mix with fluids from the seminal vesicles, prostate gland, and bulbourethral glands.
4. Clean external organs daily, abstain from sexual activity, wear a protector during athletic activities, examine testes for signs of cancer, and get regular medical exams.
5. unhealthy sperm, too few sperm
6. testes, epididymis, vas deferens, seminal vesicles, prostate gland
7. *Sample answer:* You could make young men aware of how often testicular cancer occurs in their age group by sharing statistics on the disease in teens.

The Female Reproductive System

Section 2

Objectives
- ▶ **Describe** three functions of the female reproductive system.
- ▶ **Summarize** the stages of the menstrual cycle.
- ▶ **Identify** five ways to keep the female reproductive system healthy.

Vocabulary
- **ova**
- **ovaries**
- **estrogen**
- **progesterone**
- **ovulation**
- **fallopian tubes**
- **uterus**
- **vagina**
- **hymen**
- **menstrual cycle**
- **menopause**
- **vaginitis**
- **cystitis**
- **Pap smear**
- **mammogram**

Warm-Up

Dear Advice Line,
I've been going to the same male doctor since I was a little kid. My doctor is really nice, but since my body started developing, I just don't feel comfortable having my checkups with him anymore. I'd like to see a female doctor. Is it OK to feel this way? What should I do?

WRITING Do you think this girl's feelings are normal? Write back with your advice.

Structure and Function

You learned that the reproductive cells in males are called sperm. In females, they are called eggs, or **ova** (singular, *ovum*). **The functions of the female reproductive system are to produce sex hormones, to produce eggs, and to provide a nourishing environment in which a fertilized egg can develop into a baby.**

Ovaries Look at Figure 7 on page 28 to see the organs of the female reproductive system. The reproductive glands in which eggs are produced are called **ovaries.** The ovaries are located a few inches below the waist, one on each side of the body. Each ovary is about the size of an almond. The ovaries have two important functions: they produce the female sex hormones estrogen and progesterone, and they release mature egg cells. The sex hormone **estrogen** activates certain physical changes at puberty, such as breast development, and controls the maturation of eggs. **Progesterone** activates changes to a woman's reproductive system before and during pregnancy.

When a girl is born, each ovary contains hundreds of thousands of immature eggs. The eggs begin to mature, or ripen, when the girl reaches puberty. Once puberty begins, one of the ovaries releases a ripened egg about once every month in a process called **ovulation.** The tiny egg that is released is no larger than the period at the end of this sentence.

Section 2

The Female Reproductive System

Objectives
Before class begins, write the objectives on the board. Have students copy the objectives into their notebooks at the start of class.

1. Focus

Warm-Up Advice Line

After students finish writing, call on a few volunteers to share what they wrote. Try to use their answers to make the point that such feelings are normal for both males and females after puberty. Tell students they will learn in this section why females should see a doctor for regular reproductive system checkups after reaching puberty.

2. Teach

Structure and Function

L3 Journal Writing
Ask students to write a journal entry in which they explain why it is important for a person of their gender to know about the female reproductive system. Tell students they may keep their journal entries confidential. If male students have trouble thinking of reasons, point out that most males have female loved ones whose health concerns them. Thinking of reasons for learning about a topic may help motivate students to learn about it and relate it to their own lives. **WRITING**

Sensitive Issues
- Students of both sexes may feel uncomfortable discussing much of the material covered in this section. Most girls will have some surface knowledge of the facts of menstruation and the changes of puberty, but may also hold some misconceptions. Boys are likely to be less knowledgeable about these subjects. And both boys and girls will be inexperienced in discussing reproductive functions, especially in a classroom.
- It is best to present the factual material in a straightforward manner to dispel any misconceptions and to fill any gaps in the student's knowledge. The goal should be to make students feel comfortable discussing normal bodily processes.
- If students realize that these processes need not be secrets, it may be easier for them to talk to a doctor, parent, or other trusted adult about personal sexual concerns.

EL Building Vocabulary

Write the following words on the board: ovary, fallopian tubes, testes, uterus, cervix, vagina. Call on a student to circle the word that does not belong. (*testes*) Then, ask students to write definitions for the uncircled words and explain how they are related. **WRITING**

Connect to Your Life Possible sources of reliable information include encyclopedias, medical reference books, Web sites of universities and hospitals, and medical professionals such as doctors and nurses.

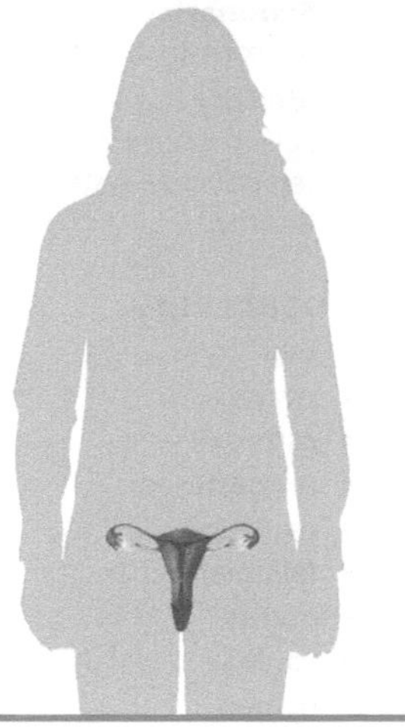

Fallopian Tubes Figure 7 also shows the location of the two **fallopian tubes** (fuh LOH pee un)—passageways that carry eggs away from the ovaries. When the ovary releases an egg during ovulation, the fingerlike ends of the fallopian tube draw the egg into the tube. Eggs, unlike sperm, cannot swim. Tiny hairlike extensions called cilia line the fallopian tube and sweep the egg toward the uterus. If sperm are present around the egg, it may be fertilized. The fallopian tubes are where fertilization usually occurs.

Uterus The **uterus** is a hollow, muscular, pear-shaped organ. In the uterus, a fertilized egg can develop and grow. The uterus has several layers of tissue and a rich supply of blood that protect and nourish the developing baby.

The narrow base of the uterus is called the cervix. When a baby is ready to be born, the cervix softens and expands to allow the baby to pass through to the vagina.

Vagina The **vagina,** or birth canal, is a hollow, muscular passage leading from the uterus to the outside of the body. Sperm enter a female's body through the vagina. During childbirth, the baby passes out of the mother's body through the vagina. The walls of the vagina are very elastic, which allows it to expand dramatically during childbirth.

Connect to Your Life **Where could you find reliable information about the female reproductive system?**

Female Reproductive System

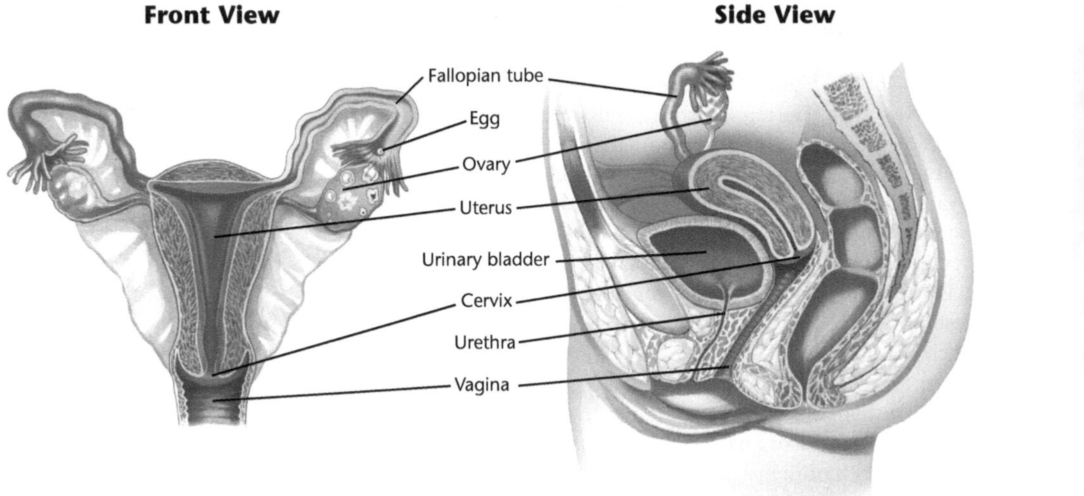

Differentiated Instruction

L2 Less Proficient Readers

Have students make a table to help them review the internal structures of the female reproductive system. In their table, they should create three columns, labeled *Structure, Description*, and *Function.* In the first column, have them list *Ovaries, Fallopian Tubes, Uterus*, and *Vagina*. Then ask them to write a description and list the functions of each organ.

External Organs The locations of the external female reproductive organs are shown below. At the base of the abdomen on top of the pubic bone is a soft, fatty tissue known as the mons pubis (mahnz PYOO bis). At puberty, the mons pubis becomes covered with pubic hair.

Below the mons pubis and surrounding the vaginal opening are two folds of soft skin. The outer folds are known as the outer labia (LAY bee uh), or the labia majora. The outer labia are covered with pubic hair. The inner folds, known as the inner labia or the labia minora, contain many nerve endings and are sensitive to touch.

Another highly sensitive organ, the clitoris, is located within the inner labia. The clitoris plays a major role in female sexual arousal and contains many nerve endings and blood vessels.

In females, orgasm is marked by rhythmic contractions of the muscles of the vagina and pelvis. Not all females have orgasms. The lack of orgasm has no effect on the ability to reproduce. A female can become pregnant with or without orgasm.

Just below the clitoris is a small opening that leads to the urethra, the tube through which urine leaves the body. Unlike in the male, the urethra is not part of the female reproductive system. Below the urethral opening is the separate opening to the vagina.

The vaginal opening may be partly covered with a thin membrane known as the **hymen** (HY mun). The hymen usually has several openings in it, which allow for the passage of menstrual flow. The hymen may tear for various reasons, including vigorous exercise, tampon insertion, or sexual intercourse. Some girls are born without a hymen.

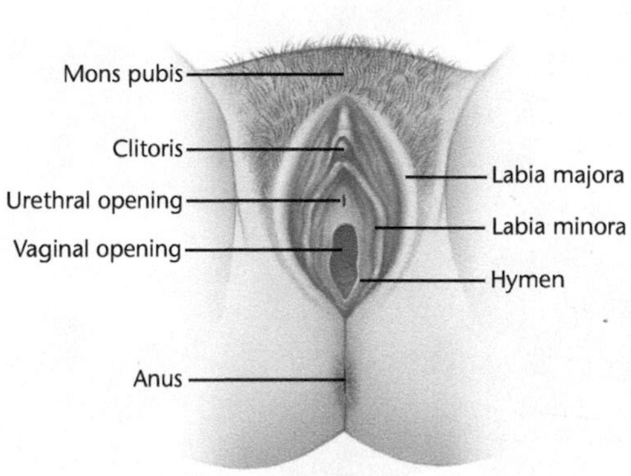

FIGURE 7 The female reproductive system produces eggs and provides a nourishing environment in which a fertilized egg can develop. **Interpreting Diagrams** Which organ releases mature eggs into the fallopian tube?

L3 Building Health Skills

Accessing Information Have students use outside resources to write at least three interesting "Did you know..." facts about the female reproductive system. The facts should not be stated in the text. Collect the facts to assure their validity and to select appropriate ones to discuss in class. If any of the "facts" students collected are actually myths, be sure to discuss these with the class. Be sensitive not to reveal who revealed the submissions, as this may cause embarrassment for some students.

L2 Visual Learning: Figure 7

Image Bank Figure 18-7

Have students use the figure to trace the path of an egg from an ovary through a fallopian tube to the uterus. Make sure they understand how the front and side views of the female reproductive system are related.

Caption Answer Ovary

TEENS *Are Asking . . .*

Q: My friend said that using tampons would make me lose my virginity. Is this true?

A: No. The term *virgin* describes a person who has not had sexual intercourse. Some girls think that an intact hymen indicates virginity and fear that using a tampon will tear the hymen. Tampons do not usually tear a hymen. Even so, the absence of a hymen or a torn hymen does not necessarily indicate that a female has had intercourse.

Chapter 2, Section 2

Concerns at Puberty

L3 Journal Writing

Have the girls in your class write a private journal entry about any concerns they have about their changing bodies. Tell them that if any of their concerns are not addressed by what they read in the text, they can talk to their doctor. Have students use their journal entries to create a list of questions for the doctor. In most cases, the doctor will reassure them that what they are going through is perfectly normal. **WRITING**

L3 Building Health Skills

Analyzing Influences Lead a class discussion about the ways that the media and popular culture affect girls' concerns about breast size. Have students give examples of media images that fuel the concerns (*For example, busty models in magazines; lowcut clothing worn by TV/movie/pop stars*) Then have the class discuss how girls can "tune out" influences that might make them feel inadequate (*For example, the knowledge that photos are often retouched; many models/actresses have had "breast augmentation" surgery; many actresses who play teens on TV are actually in their twenties or thirties, so are further along in their development*)

Concerns at Puberty

Most girls have many questions and concerns about the changes that occur to their bodies during puberty.

Sexual Arousal Like most teen males, females also may notice an increase in sexual feelings during puberty. A photograph of a favorite movie star, a dream or fantasy, the presence of an attractive person, or some other stimulus may cause the heart to speed up and the breathing rate to quicken. Females may notice a feeling of wetness in and around the vagina, and may also have a swollen feeling in the pelvis. These are normal signs of sexual excitement.

Masturbation Like males, some females masturbate, or touch their own genitals to obtain sexual pleasure. Some people object to masturbation on moral or religious grounds. Most doctors agree that masturbation is harmless unless it becomes a preoccupation, makes you feel guilty, or interferes with your daily activities.

Physical Appearance One of the most common concerns of young women during puberty is breast development. In spite of what some girls believe, there is no "perfect" or "normal" breast size or shape. One breast may be a little larger than the other. The nipples may stick out or turn in. Breast size and appearance generally have no effect on the ability to feel sexual excitement or to nurse a child.

Just as breast size and shape vary from woman to woman, so does each girl's timetable for breast development. Some girls may notice breast development as early as age 8; others may not start developing until age 14 or later. It is quite normal for teen girls of the same age to be at different stages of breast development.

FIGURE 8 Teen girls, like boys, may worry about their physical appearance during puberty. Focusing on your strengths is one way to boost your self-confidence.

TEENS *Are Asking . . .*

Q: I get my period only once every 6 weeks or so, but then it usually lasts about 7 days. Is that normal, or should I be worried?

A: Generally, having shorter- or longer-than average menstrual cycles or menstrual periods is nothing to worry about, because there is a lot of normal variation in these events. Variation is especially common during adolescence. However, if your periods change from what is typical for you or you are still concerned, talk with your doctor. It probably means nothing, but it could be a sign that you are under too much stress or have an underlying health problem.

Media Wise

Sexuality in Music Videos

When watching your favorite music videos, you may not think about the hidden, or not-so-hidden, meanings they contain. What messages are conveyed about sex? Consider these questions as they relate to music videos.

1. **Are there suggestive close-ups on body parts?** Yes No
2. **Is there non-verbal flirting (such as suggestive body positions or touching)?** Yes No
3. **Does anyone dress suggestively or take off any clothing?** Yes No
4. **Does anyone use force to touch or kiss someone?** Yes No
5. **Is there sexual bias—a greater emphasis on women's or men's bodies?** Yes No

A "Yes" answer to one or more questions may indicate a video that presents sex in an unhealthy way.

Activity Think about how music videos make you feel about your body. In general, do they represent sex in a healthy or unhealthy way? Explain. **WRITING**

The Menstrual Cycle

As you learned, males typically produce millions of sperm cells every day after reaching puberty. Females, on the other hand, usually produce only one mature egg cell each month during a process called the **menstrual cycle** (MEN stroo ul). **During the menstrual cycle, an ovary releases a mature egg. The egg travels to the uterus. If the egg is not fertilized, the uterine lining is shed and a new cycle begins.**

Factors Affecting the Menstrual Cycle On average, a menstrual cycle lasts 28 days. However, cycles as short as 21 days or as long as 35 days can be normal for some individuals. The endocrine system controls the menstrual cycle. The hormones involved include FSH and LH, which are released by the pituitary gland, and estrogen and progesterone, which are released from the ovaries. Factors such as diet, stress, exercise, and weight gain or weight loss also affect the menstrual cycle. The menstrual cycle may be irregular at times, especially during puberty.

Except during pregnancy, menstrual cycles occur each month from puberty until about the age of 45 to 55. At that time of life, called **menopause,** the ovaries slow down their hormone production and no longer release mature eggs. Gradually, the menstrual cycle stops, and the woman is no longer able to become pregnant.

Differentiated Instruction

L1 Special Needs

The menstrual cycle is complex and may be confusing to many students. For special needs students, focus mainly on the two key events in the cycle: menstruation and ovulation. On the board, make a simplified diagram showing that menstruation is the bleeding that happens at the beginning of the cycle and ovulation is the release of an egg that happens in the middle of the cycle.

Media Wise

Sexuality in Music Videos

As a homework assignment, ask students to watch one of their favorite music videos and answer questions 1–5 about it. During the next class, call on students to share their answers. Try to get responses about several different music videos. Discuss why "Yes" answers to the questions may indicate that the videos present sex in unhealthy ways.

Activity After the discussion, have students do the writing activity. Tell them that they do not have to share what they write. When students finish writing, take a vote on whether they think music videos generally represent sex in a healthy or unhealthy way. Ask a few volunteers to state how they voted and explain why.

The Menstrual Cycle

L2 Building Vocabulary

Call on students to find and read aloud the definitions in the text for menstrual cycle and menstruation. Explain that the terms come from a Latin word, *mensis*, which means "month." Ask: **What is the connection between these two terms and *month*?** *(The menstrual cycle, including menstruation, repeats in approximately month-long cycles.)*

L3 Cultural Connection

Girls in many cultures and religions go through coming-of-age rituals. In Hispanic cultures, this ritual is called *quinceñeara*. In the Jewish religion, it is *bat mitzvah*. Ask students to identify other coming-of-age rituals. *(e.g., confirmation in Catholicism; African-based rituals in African-American churches and community centers)* Discuss how the rituals may help girls feel more mature by providing a clear marker of adulthood.

L2 Visual Learning: Figure 9

Image Bank Figure 18-8

Have pairs of same-gender students work together to learn the information in the figure. Give each pair five index cards. On the front of the cards, students should write the ranges of days from the figure (days 1–4, 5–13, and so on). On the back of the cards, they should list the menstrual cycle events that occur during those days of the cycle. Have partners shuffle the cards and try to put them in the correct order without looking at the days on the front. They should keep trying until they can do it correctly.

Caption Answer a fallopian tube

L2 Active Learning

Ask students to make a different kind of visual representation of the menstrual cycle that may be easier for some students to understand. The exercise may also help female students learn how to keep track of their own menstrual cycles. Make and distribute copies of a monthly calendar page for February (because it has the same number of days as the average menstrual cycle). Have students block out the five stages of the menstrual cycle on the calendar and write in specific menstrual cycle events (e.g., ovulation) on the appropriate days of the month. Display the calendars in the classroom.

L3 Addressing Misconceptions

The Menstrual Cycle and Conception

Many students will have misconceptions about pregnancy, such as believing that women can become pregnant *only* on the day of ovulation. Remind students that fertilization usually occurs in a fallopian tube. Have students use Figure 9 to find out on which days of the cycle an egg is in a fallopian tube. *(days 16–22)* Then have them infer on which days of the menstrual cycle conception is most likely. *(days 16–22)* Remind them that while a woman is most likely to get pregnant during the week surrounding ovulation, it is still *possible* for her to get pregnant at any time.

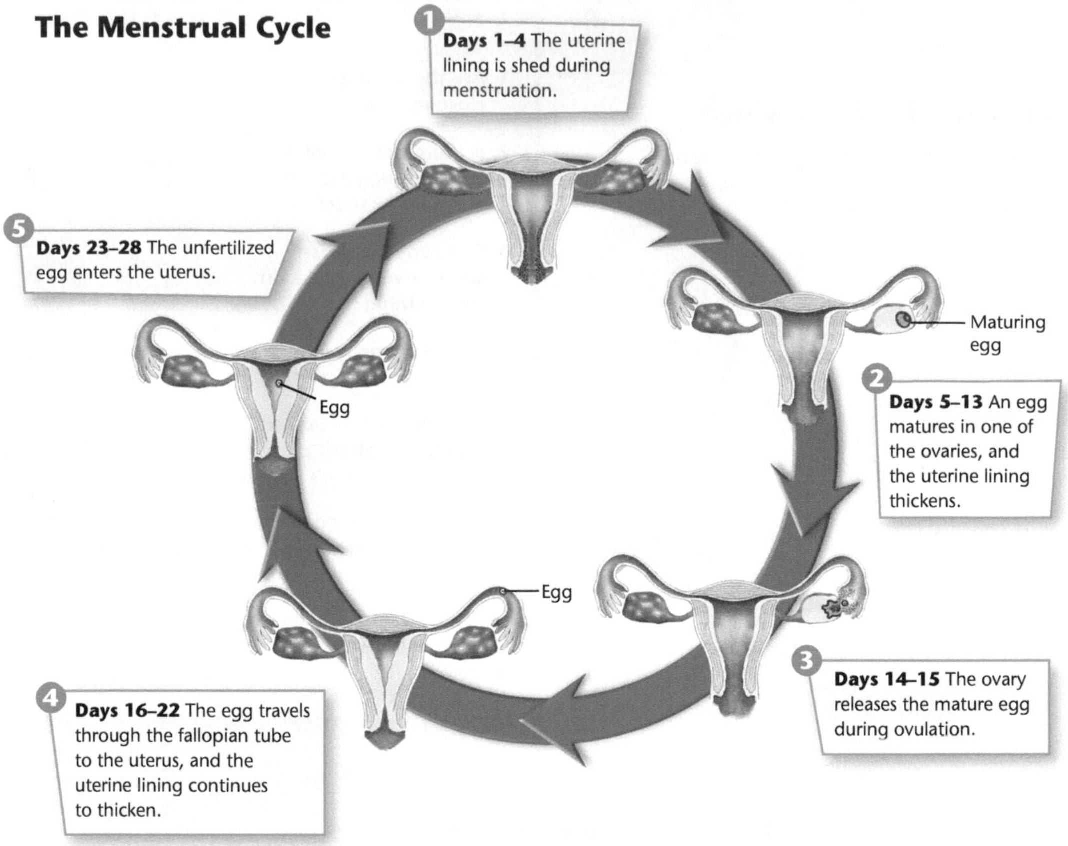

FIGURE 9 The thickening of the lining of the uterus, ovulation, and menstruation are key events of the menstrual cycle.
Interpreting Diagrams Through which structure does an egg travel before reaching the uterus?

Stages of the Menstrual Cycle Follow the stages of a typical menstrual cycle in Figure 9. During the first half of the cycle, an egg matures inside one of the ovaries. Meanwhile, the lining of the uterus thickens. At about the middle of the cycle—typically on day 14—ovulation occurs. The mature egg is released by the ovary and travels into the fallopian tube. A female is most fertile, or able to become pregnant, around the time of ovulation.

It takes about seven days for the egg to travel through the fallopian tube into the uterus. During this time the uterine lining continues to thicken, and the blood supply to it increases. If the egg has not been fertilized by the time it reaches the uterus, the uterine lining breaks down.

The blood and tissue of the thickened lining pass out of the body through the vagina in a process called menstruation, or the menstrual period. As menstruation is taking place, another egg begins to mature in one of the ovaries. Thus menstruation marks the end of one cycle and the beginning of another. In general, a menstrual period lasts about 3 to 5 days. Most women wear either a sanitary pad or a tampon to absorb the menstrual flow.

Focus on **ISSUES**

L3 Females and Medical Research

Until recently, medical research projects rarely included female subjects. Most researchers reasoned that the monthly changes of the menstrual cycle would interfere with study controls. As a result, doctors were forced to assume whatever was learned from medical research on males applied to females as well. We now know that this assumption is not always true. Recently, federal laws were passed requiring females to be included as subjects in federally funded medical research. Hold a class discussion about the issue of female subjects in medical research. Start the discussion by asking students whether they agree with the legislation and why or why not.

Menstrual Discomfort During the menstrual period, some women may experience abdominal cramps or other discomfort. Cramps are caused by contractions of the uterus. See Figure 10 for some ways to relieve menstrual cramps. For severe cramps or for any other menstrual concerns, women should see a medical professional.

Some women experience discomfort some time before the menstrual period. This condition, known as premenstrual syndrome, or PMS, is marked by nervous tension, mood swings, headaches, bloating, and irritability. The dramatic change in hormone levels that occurs before menstruation begins may cause PMS. Some doctors recommend that PMS sufferers reduce their intake of salt, sugar, and caffeine, get regular exercise, and try other stress-reduction techniques.

Toxic Shock Syndrome A rare but serious medical condition associated with tampon use is toxic shock syndrome. This syndrome is caused by a bacterial infection. Symptoms of toxic shock syndrome include a sudden high fever, a rash, vomiting, diarrhea, and dizziness. Because toxic shock syndrome can lead to death, a woman with any of these symptoms during her period should seek medical attention immediately. To decrease the risk of toxic shock syndrome, women should use tampons with the lowest possible absorbency for their needs and change tampons often.

Connect to Your Life **What misconceptions did you hold about menstruation before reading this section?**

GO ONLINE
PearsonSuccessNet.com
For: More on the menstrual cycle

Menstrual cramps? Try this . . .
- Engage in moderate exercise.
- Take a warm bath.
- Apply a heating pad to the abdomen.
- Take aspirin or ibuprofen with doctor's approval.

FIGURE 10 Following these simple tips can help relieve menstrual cramps.

L3 Online Activity GO ONLINE

Visit Pearson SuccessNet to access an online activity about the menstrual cycle. Have students complete the Web activity.

L2 Cooperative Learning

Ask groups of several students each to brainstorm three lists: factors that can influence menstruation *(stress, illness, change in weight)*; discomforts that may accompany menstruation *(cramps, mood swings, bloating)*; and possible ways to treat the discomforts *(heating pads, pain medication, exercise)*. Give groups a chance to share their lists.

L3 Building Media Literacy

Have students find examples of television, print, or Internet ads for products that claim to relieve menstrual discomforts. Ask students to write a paragraph examining the claims made in the ads. Do they think the claims are reliable or misleading? Why? **WRITING**

Connect to Your Life Allow students to answer this question in their private journals.

Differentiated Instruction

EL English Language Learners

Help students develop the skill of using context clues to determine the meanings of new words. First, work through an example to show students how. Point out the word *period* in the first sentence on this page. Read aloud from a dictionary at least two definitions of *period,* including the correct one. Ask students to select the correct definition, based on the word's context. Ask: **What other word in the sentence is a clue to the correct meaning of *period?*** *(menstrual)* Have students write down words on this page that they do not recognize. Have them look up the words in a dictionary and try to choose the correct definitions based on the context.

Keeping Healthy

L2 Building Health Skills

Advocacy Have groups of students make posters conveying to other teens how and why to care for the female reproductive system. Students should illustrate each healthy habit listed in the text with a tasteful cartoon, sketch, or magazine photo to make the posters interesting and eye-catching. Arrange to display the posters at school in the girls' locker rooms and restrooms.

L1 Cooperative Learning

Divide the class into same-gender groups, and have members of each group work together to express the five healthy habits as lists of "Do's" and "Don'ts." *(For example, for cleanliness, students might list: "Do shower daily;" and "don't use deodorant tampons.")* Give groups a chance to share their lists. Select one "Do" and one "Don't" statement about each habit. Call on students to explain how following the "Do's" and "Don'ts" contributes to good health.

L3 Active Learning

Have interested students contact a medical professional in their community to find out at what age females should start having Pap smears to detect cervical cancer. Appropriate medical professionals might include a school nurse, a nurse in a gynecologist's office, or the director of a local chapter of the American Cancer Society. Ask students to share what they learn with the class. Discuss how detecting cancer early with Pap smears improves chances of survival.

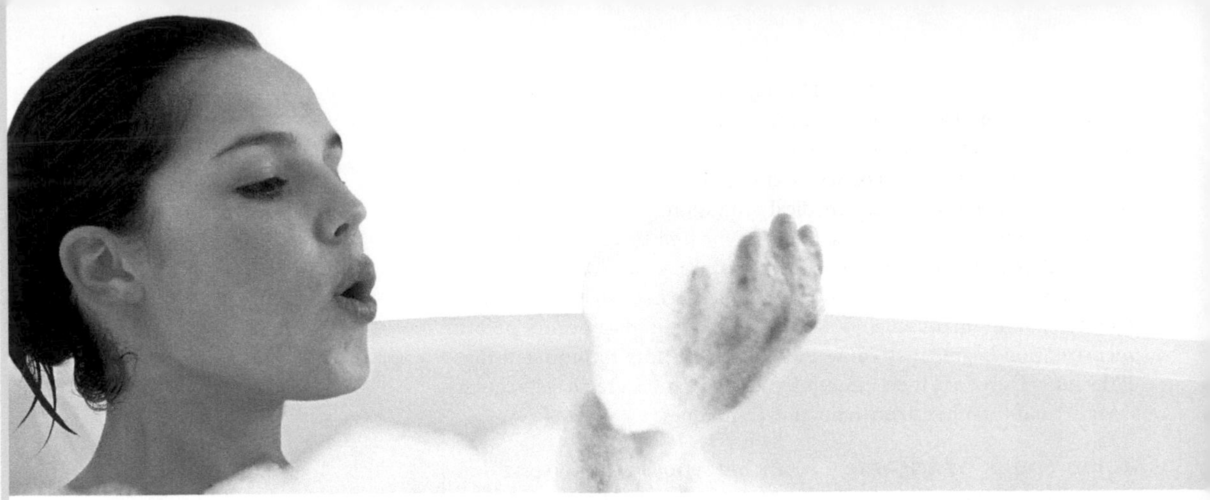

FIGURE 11 Daily washing is an important part of keeping the reproductive system healthy.

Keeping Healthy

A number of medical conditions can affect the female reproductive system. Teens who adopt healthy habits can reduce their risk of problems. **Caring for the female reproductive system involves cleanliness, sexual abstinence, prompt treatment for infections, self-exams, and regular medical checkups.**

Cleanliness One important health habit is cleanliness, including daily washing of the external vaginal area. Cleanliness is especially important during menstruation, as is the regular changing of sanitary pads or tampons. Feminine hygiene sprays, douches, and deodorant tampons are not necessary. In fact, they may be harmful if they cover up signs of an infection or cause irritation. If washing does not get rid of normal body odors, or if any unusual discharge is noted, seek medical attention.

Sexual Abstinence A number of serious infections can result from sexual contact. Healthy choices regarding sexual behavior can prevent such infections. The only way to eliminate your risk of sexually transmitted infections is to abstain from sexual activity.

Prompt Treatment for Infections Some infections of the reproductive system are not related to sexual behavior. Many women experience **vaginitis,** a vaginal infection caused by yeast, bacteria, or other microorganisms. Symptoms can include an unusual discharge or odors, itching, and a burning sensation during urination. Only a doctor can diagnose the specific cause of vaginitis and provide appropriate treatment.

Another common problem among females is **cystitis** (sih STY tis), an infection of the bladder. Cystitis is caused by bacteria that travel up the urethra into the bladder. Symptoms include the urge to urinate frequently and a burning sensation during urination. If you experience these symptoms, you should consult a doctor. If left untreated, cystitis can lead to a kidney infection or even permanent kidney damage.

TEENS *Are Asking . . .*

Q: What is the difference between a Pap smear and a gynecologic exam? When should I start having them? I'm a 15-year-old girl.

A: You are not alone if you are confused about Pap smears and gynecologic exams. A recent study found that many teenaged girls and young women think that a Pap smear is the same thing as a gynecologic exam. Only 2 percent of girls in the study knew the difference. Experts fear this misconception may lead young women to delay their first gynecologic exam until after they become sexually active. A Pap smear is a test only for cervical cancer. A gynecologic exam is a more general checkup of the reproductive system. It may or may not include a Pap smear. According to new recommendations from the Centers for Disease Control, girls should have their first gynecologic exam between the ages of 13 and 15 and their first Pap smear two years after they become sexually active.

Self-Exams It is important for females to monitor their own bodies for signs of possible medical problems. Symptoms of vaginitis or cystitis, sores on the genitals, or any unusual pain in the abdomen require a medical exam. A female should also consult a doctor if she notices heavier bleeding than normal during menstruation, if her periods stop completely, or if she notices bleeding at times in between her regular periods.

Teen girls and women should also examine their breasts on a monthly basis for signs of breast cancer, one of the most common forms of cancer in females. Breast cancer is rare in teens, but it becomes more common as women age. The teen years are a good time to establish a lifetime habit of regular breast self-exams. If breast cancer is found early, the disease can be treated effectively and often cured.

Figure 12 outlines the procedure for the breast self-exam. The best time to do a breast self-exam is the week after a menstrual period, when the breasts are least swollen. For females who have not yet started menstruating, who have irregular periods, or who have reached menopause, the exam should be done on the same day each month. If you forget a month, don't worry. Resume the regular exams once you remember.

FIGURE 12 Females should follow this procedure to perform the breast self-exam.
Interpreting Diagrams Describe the motion that is recommended for ensuring that the entire breast area is checked.

Breast Self-Exam

1 Check your breasts while lying down.

- Lie down and place your right arm behind your head. Use the finger pads of the three middle fingers on your left hand to feel for lumps in the right breast.
- Use overlapping, dime-sized circular motions of the finger pads and three different levels of pressure. Use light pressure to feel the tissue closest to the skin. Use medium pressure to feel a little deeper. Use firm pressure to feel the tissue closest to the chest and ribs.
- Feel the breast in an up-and-down pattern starting at an imaginary line drawn straight down your side from the underarm (see diagram). Move inward until you reach your sternum, the bone in the middle of your chest.
- Check the entire breast area, moving down until you can feel only ribs, and moving up to your collar bone.
- Continue lying down. Lower your right hand and place your left arm above your head. Repeat the exam on your left breast, using the finger pads of the right hand.

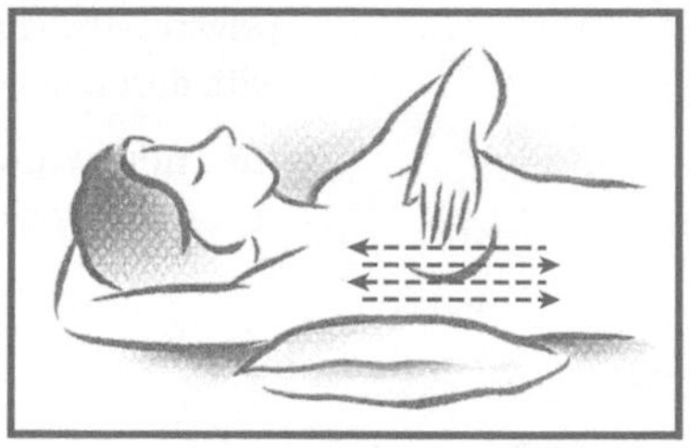

2 Look at your breasts while standing in front of a mirror.
While pressing your hands down firmly on your hips, look for any change in breast shape or appearance, such as dimpling of the skin, redness or swelling, or changes to the nipples.

3 Examine each underarm.
While standing or sitting, slightly raise your right arm and feel your underarm with your lefthand fingers. Repeat on your left side.

4 Report any abnormalities to your doctor immediately.
Many lumps are cysts or harmless tumors that are not cancerous, but only a doctor can make a diagnosis.

L2 Visual Learning: Figure 12

Have students make a simplified outline of the steps of the breast self-exam to help them process the detailed information and make the steps easier to recall. **Caption Answer** up-and-down from the ribs to the collar bone, and side-to-side from the underarm to the sternum

L1 Active Learning

Some doctors have models of breasts with lumps. If possible, borrow a model and let female students practice using the three levels of pressure and the up-and-down motion to examine the model and to experience what a lump might feel like. Discuss why doing the exam monthly gives girls or women good familiarity with the "normal" feel of their breasts, so that they can more easily detect an abnormality should one arise. Doing the exam monthly can also help to catch a potential tumor while it is still small and treatment is more effective.

L2 Building Health Skills

Advocacy Point out that self-exams save lives by detecting cancer early. However, many people have a hard time remembering to do self-exams. Challenge groups of students to think of ways they could remember to do regular self-exams. (*Possible ways might include noting when to do self-exams on a calendar, asking a friend or family member to remind them, or posting a reminder on the bathroom mirror or in the shower.*)

Differentiated Instruction

L4 Gifted and Talented

Some students may be curious about the medical processes that would be used to make a diagnosis after a self-exam reveals a suspicious lump. How does a doctor determine whether a lump is benign or malignant? Volunteer some of your students who need a challenge to find out what procedures (such as biopsy) are used. Have them report what they learn to the class. They may also like to report back on the various treatments used to fight breast cancer.

3. Assess

Evaluate

These assignments can help you assess students' mastery of the section content.

L3 Section 2 Review

Answers appear below.

L2 Reteach

Have students draw sketches of the female reproductive system and the menstrual cycle. Ask students to label their sketches with a brief description of each part.

L4 Enrich

Health at School

Medication Regulations Most schools have written policies regarding medications. Students may also find the policies in their student handbook. Call on a few volunteers to read their memos. Discuss reasons for the policies.

FIGURE 13 This doctor is using a magnifying glass to more closely examine a mammogram. A mammogram may detect cancers that are too small for a woman or her doctor to feel in a breast exam.

Medical Checkups A yearly checkup of the reproductive system is recommended for all females who have reached puberty. During the exam, the doctor will examine the breasts and genitals. The doctor is also likely to perform a pelvic exam if the female is over 18 or sexually active.

During the pelvic exam, the doctor inserts two gloved fingers into the vagina and places the other hand on the patient's abdomen. This way the doctor can feel the size and shape of the uterus and ovaries and check for any swelling, growths, or tenderness. The doctor may also perform a **Pap smear,** a test for cervical cancer. The doctor inserts an instrument called a speculum into the vagina, which holds the walls of the vagina apart. Next the doctor gently scrapes some cells from the cervix. The cells are sent to a laboratory and examined under a microscope for signs of cancer.

Starting at about age 40, women may get a **mammogram,** an X-ray of the breast that can help detect breast cancer. A woman with a family history of breast cancer or other risk factors may have her first mammogram at a younger age.

A doctor can also detect and treat other reproductive problems, including cancers of the ovary or uterus, and the following:

- **Ovarian cysts** Ovarian cysts are growths on the ovary. Large ones may be painful and need to be surgically removed.
- **Endometriosis** This is a condition in which tissue from the lining of the uterus—the endometrium—grows outside the uterus, in the pelvic cavity. This condition can be very painful and is usually treated with hormones or surgery.
- **Infertility** Causes of infertility in women include blocked fallopian tubes and problems with ovulation.

Section 2 Review

Key Ideas and Vocabulary

1. What are three main functions of the female reproductive system?
2. What is **ovulation**?
3. What event marks the end of one menstrual cycle and the beginning of another?
4. List five things that females should do to maintain reproductive health.

Critical Thinking

5. **Calculating** If a woman's ovaries release one egg per month for 30 years, how many eggs in total will she have released? MATH

Health at School

Medication Regulations Many girls suffer from menstrual cramps, sometimes during school hours. Ask your school nurse or an administrator what the policies are for taking pain medications on school grounds to treat menstrual cramps and other common aches and pains. Write a memo detailing your findings. WRITING

6. **Applying Concepts** How could more young women be convinced of the importance of regular breast self-exams? WRITING

Section 2 Review

1. to produce sex hormones, to produce eggs, and to provide a nourishing environment in which a fertilized egg can develop into a baby
2. the release of a ripened egg by an ovary
3. menstruation
4. Keep clean, abstain from sexual activity, get prompt treatment for infections, do regular self-exams, and get yearly checkups.
5. 360 eggs
6. *Sample answer:* They could be convinced by information about the risk of breast cancer and how early detection saves lives.

Chapter 2 Review

VIDEO **TEENS Talk**
Taking Charge of Your Health In what ways did the video motivate you to take charge of your health?

Reviewing Key Ideas

Section 1

1. Which of the following is *not* a structure in the male reproductive system?
   a. epididymis b. seminal vesicle
   c. uterus d. vas deferens
2. In males, straining to lift heavy objects may result in
   a. an inguinal hernia.
   b. an enlarged prostate.
   c. testicular cancer.
   d. infertility.
3. For which of the following should a male seek immediate medical attention?
   a. erections for no apparent reason
   b. testicular torsion
   c. nocturnal emission
   d. breast tenderness
4. What are the reproductive glands called in males?
5. What are two effects of testosterone?
6. Describe the roles played by hormones during sperm production.
7. Describe the route of sperm from the testes to the penis.
8. List three possible causes of infertility in men.
9. **Critical Thinking** Steroids abused by some athletes to build muscle contain chemicals similar to sex hormones. Why do you think steroid use can have a harmful effect on the reproductive system, especially in teens?
10. **Critical Thinking** Only one sperm is needed to fertilize an egg, yet millions of sperm are released during ejaculation. Why do you think this is?

Section 2

11. Which organ releases mature eggs?
    a. hymen b. pituitary gland
    c. vagina d. ovary
12. How long is the average menstrual cycle?
    a. 3 to 5 days b. 14 days
    c. 28 days d. 9 months
13. Explain how the functions of the uterus and cervix are related.
14. In which reproductive structure does fertilization usually take place?
15. Name two hormones that play a role in the menstrual cycle.
16. Which kind of cancer may be detected by a Pap smear?
17. **Critical Thinking** Your 13-year-old sister does not menstruate regularly. Should she be concerned? Explain.

Building Health Skills

18. **Accessing Information** Suppose that your younger brother is worried because he's been hearing a lot of myths about puberty from his classmates. How could you help him find accurate information?
19. **Advocacy** Suppose that a friend has confided in you that during a breast self-exam, she detected a lump. She is reluctant to see a doctor. Write an e-mail to your friend with advice. **WRITING**
20. **Communicating** What kinds of questions might a teenager want to ask the doctor during puberty? Make a list of possible questions for someone of your gender.
21. **Practicing Healthful Behaviors** What important health decisions can you make to keep your reproductive system healthy? Describe at least three decisions and explain what positive effect those decisions can have. **WRITING**

Health and Community

Cancer Awareness Write a script for a public service announcement to raise awareness about prostate or breast cancer. Think about the age of the people you want to target with your message. Develop your message to best reach that audience. **WRITING**

Chapter 2 Review

Reviewing Key Ideas

Section 1

1. c 2. a 3. b 4. testes
5. production of sperm and physical changes in males at puberty
6. LH signals the testes to make testosterone. Testosterone and FSH trigger the production of sperm.
7. *Sample answer:* Sperm are produced in the testes, mature in the epididymis, and travel through the vas deferens to the accessory glands. They travel through the penis during ejaculation.
8. exposure to certain chemicals, developing mumps after puberty, and undescended tesits
9. *Sample answer:* Because steroids are similar to sex hormones, they might interfere with the proper development and functioning of the reproductive system in teens.
10. A large number of sperm raises the chances of successful fertilization.

Section 2

11. d 12. c
13. *Sample answer:* The uterus carries the developing embryo and fetus during pregnancy. The cervix at the base of the uterus softens and expands at the end of pregnancy, allowing the baby to be born.
14. fallopian tubes
15. *Any two:* LH, FSH, estrogen, progesterone
16. cancer of the cervix
17. *Sample answer:* She should not be concerned because menstruation often is irregular during puberty.

Building Health Skills

18. Answers should include at least one reliable source of accurate information, such as a medical reference book.
19. In their e-mails, students should try to persuade the friend to see a doctor. They might stress how early detection and treatment is critical.
20. Allow students to keep their answers private.
21. Answers will vary, but should draw from the "Keeping Healthy" section (on pages 24–26 for boys and 34–36 for girls).

Health and Community

Cancer Awareness Students' PSAs should be informative and convincing, and they should incorporate accurate information relevant to the age group they are targeting. Students might target people over age 40 or 50, because breast and prostate cancer are more common in these age groups.

CHAPTER 3

Chapter Preview

Section 1 Dating Relationships
Dating, either in a group or as a couple, provides an opportunity to learn about another person's personality, interests, abilities, and values. Knowing what to expect on a date can make the experience less awkward.

Section 2 Choosing Abstinence
The risks of sexual intimacy include the risk of pregnancy and the risk of sexually transmitted infections. Teens who choose abstinence need to set clear limits, communicate those limits, avoid high-pressure situations, and assert themselves.

Section 3 Unhealthy Relationships
Violence in dating relationships can include physical, emotional, and sexual abuse. A major reason that people abuse others is the need for control. Abuse needs to be reported.

Section 4 Sexual Issues in Society
There are rules teens should follow to protect themselves when they use the Internet. Teens may become involved with prostitution and pornography because they need money to survive or because they are lured into these activities by false promises.

National Health Education Standards Correlation

1.12.5, 2.12.1, 2.12.5, 2.12.6, 2.12.7, 2.12.8, 2.12.9, 4.12.1, 4.12.2, 5.12.1, 5.12.2, 5.12.5, 5.12.6, 7.12.1, 7.12.3

Chapter 3

Responsible Relationships

GO ONLINE PearsonSuccessNet.com

TEENS Talk

Choosing Abstinence

Preview **Activity**

What Do Your Choices Say About You?

Complete this activity before you watch the video.

1. Think about this quote.
   It is our choices that show what we truly are, far more than our abilities.
2. Then write a short paragraph describing what the quote means to you. **WRITING**
3. Pair up with another student to share and discuss your paragraphs.

GO ONLINE
PearsonSuccessNet.com
For resources and activities for this chapter.

Sensitive Issues

- Abstinence can be a difficult topic for students, especially if they are already sexually active. Don't require students to participate in a discussion if they are uncomfortable with the topic.
- Never ask students to disclose information they would rather keep confidential.
- Students who have been abused may want to talk with you. In some cases, you might need to consult with the guidance counselor, school nurse, principal, or other school officials to avoid legal problems. In all states, teachers are mandated reporters of suspected abuse and neglect.

39

VIDEO 6

TEENS Talk

Choosing Abstinence

Video Objectives

Use this video to help students

Recognize the risks of sexual intimacy and the benefits of choosing abstinence.

Develop the decision-making and communication skills they need to resist the pressure to have sex.

Identify ways to avoid high-pressure situations.

Preview **Activity**

What Do Your Choices Say About You?

Assign the Preview Activity for homework a few days before you plan to show the video. Just before you show the video, have pairs of students discuss their responses. Then, as a class, review the role that values play in decision making.

From the Authors

As a teacher, you have an opportunity to reinforce the message of abstinence that teens hear from parents and clergy by stressing the value of abstinence to health. For teens, sexual abstinence is a behavior that makes good sense from a public health standpoint because it is a protective factor against unwanted pregnancy and sexually transmitted infections.

Because national data suggest that you will be teaching many students who have already become sexually involved, you can also stress the value of a return to abstinence. The Health at Home activity on page 48 is designed to encourage dialogue about sexual decisions between students and adult family members.

ABILITY LEVELS
L1 For students with special needs
L2 For less proficient readers
L3 For all students
L4 For gifted and talented students
EL For English language learners

Section 1

Dating Relationships

Objectives
Before class begins, write the objectives on the board. Have students copy the objectives into their notebooks at the start of class.

1. Focus

***Warm-Up* Quick**

Give students several minutes to read the choices and select a response. Then have students complete the writing assignment. For each possible quiz response, ask a volunteer who selected that response to share his or her writing with the class. Remind students that there are no right or wrong responses to this quiz.

Sensitive Issues

- If the norm at your school is for students to date, students who are not dating may be uncomfortable with discussions on dating.
- Be respectful of the variety of cultural and family practices regarding dating.
- Discuss hypothetical situations that might occur in dating relationships rather than asking students to relate personal experiences.

Section 1 Dating Relationships

Objectives

- **List** some things you can learn about a person by dating.
- **Describe** some strategies for dealing with dating concerns.

Vocabulary

- **infatuation**

Warm-Up

Quick Quiz Which of these do you value most in a romantic partner?

1. **Someone who is physically attractive**
2. **Someone who is outgoing**
3. **Someone who is intelligent**
4. **Someone who is honest and reliable**
5. **Someone who shares my values**

WRITING Explain why you selected the answer that you did.

Physical Attraction and Dating

The teenage years are a time when most young people begin to experience feelings of physical attraction. Have you ever had a "crush" on a movie star, athlete, teacher, or other person you admire? Most teenagers have. Another name for these feelings of intense attraction to another person is **infatuation.** Although these feelings can sometimes be overwhelming, they are normal and healthy for teenagers. From these feelings, you develop the ability to form close attachments later in your adult life.

When you are attracted to someone, you want to spend time with that person. Some people use the term *dating* to describe the time you spend together. **By dating someone, you can learn about his or her interests, personality, abilities, and values.** You can also learn how the other person views the gender roles that he or she learned as a child. You may even discover what qualities you want in a future marriage partner.

Dating practices vary with individuals, families, and cultures. Some teens don't date at all during high school because they don't want to or because dating is not permitted in their culture. When teens do date, some stick to traditional practices. For example, females may wait for males to ask them out, or expect the males to pay for the date. Today, however, many dating arrangements are more informal than in the past.

For Your INFORMATION!

Dating Statistics

From 1976 to 2004, the percentage of high school seniors who said they didn't date increased from 15 percent to 27 percent. Today's teens are more likely to go out in mixed-gender groups. About 27 percent of seniors are frequent daters who have at least one formal date each week. Teens who are frequent daters typically have poorer grades and report more conflict with parents than do those who go out in groups.

Hanging Out and Talking People who are physically attracted to each other often begin to recognize that attraction when they hang out together for lengthy periods of time. Talking (and listening) can be a great way to get to know someone. Hanging out and talking can also occur in groups. There are advantages to hanging out as a group. It gives you an opportunity to see how people behave when they are with others. In return, the person you are attracted to can get to know more about you.

Going Out as Couples You may discover that you especially enjoy being with a certain friend. The person may be someone who shares your interests or has a similar sense of humor. You also may be physically attracted to this person. It is natural and healthy to feel physical attraction and to want to get to know the person better. This may lead to dating, either on your own or with other couples.

Dating After a few dates, a couple may decide not to go out with other people and to see each other on a regular basis. Dating a person exclusively can be a form of security—partners are assured of having someone to hang out with.

Exclusive dating has some drawbacks. You limit your chances of meeting other people you might like. You may feel pressured to make decisions about sexual intimacy before you are ready. If conflicts arise, it may be difficult to break off the relationship.

For some couples, exclusive dating leads to marriage. For couples who marry as teens, there are challenges beyond those faced by most married couples. These challenges may include a lack of emotional maturity, loss of freedom, and loss of shared activities with friends.

Connect to Your Life **Do you think exclusive dating during high school is a good idea? Why or why not?**

FIGURE 1 If you go out as a group or as couples, you get to know many different people. You also get to observe how a person who you are attracted to interacts with others.

2. Teach

Physical Attraction and Dating

L2 Active Learning

Explain that dating is a way to learn about another person's personality, interests, abilities, and values. Distribute four index cards to each student. Tell students that their responses will be kept confidential. Ask students to write the word *personality* on the front of one card. On the back of the card, have students identify and record three personality traits they would find attractive in a person they might date. Have students complete similar cards titled *interests, abilities,* and *values*. Have a class discussion on the importance of thinking in advance about what qualities you might want in a date.

L3 Addressing Misconceptions

Teens and Dating Students may have the misconception that all teens date. Point out that many teens do not date, either by choice or due to cultural or family expectations. Some studies have found 37 percent of tenth graders and 25 percent of twelfth graders don't date.

EL Cultural Connection

Have students do brief, informal presentations about dating customs in their cultures. Encourage students to bring photographs or other objects to help them explain the customs.

Connect to Your Life *Sample answer:* I think steady dating during high school is not a good idea because it often leads to pressure for sexual intimacy.

Differentiated Instruction

L2 Less Proficient Readers

Have less proficient readers work as partners with advanced readers to prepare an outline of the material in this section. Have students use the boldface heads in the section as the main headings in their outlines. Under each heading, have students record key ideas, supporting details, and relevant vocabulary terms. Encourage students to review their outlines after they have completed the section and add information under each heading that will enhance their understanding of the content.

Media Wise

Gender Roles and Movies

Although gender roles in the United States are less clearly defined now than they were in the past, students will probably be able to identify examples of traditional gender roles in current movies. Interested students may want to extend the activity by analyzing and comparing the way that gender roles are portrayed in movies from different eras.

Activity Ask volunteers to share their summaries with the class. Then have students indicate by a show of hands if they feel that movies influence people's opinions about gender roles. Have students provide examples to support their opinions.

Dating Concerns

L3 Journal Writing

Ask students to think of a time when they were tempted to "put on an act." Have them record an entry in their private journals describing the situation, the decision they made, and the effects of that decision. **WRITING**

L1 Class Discussion

Tell students that rejection is a type of setback. Discuss strategies for dealing with a setback, such as monitoring and refuting negative "self-talk" and treating the rejection as an isolated event.

L4 Building Health Skills

Accessing Information Have interested students interview a few adults about what it was like to date when they were young. After students complete the interviews, have them write a brief summary of what they learned. Ask them to compare and contrast the dating practices of earlier generations with those of their generation. **WRITING**

Connect to Your Life Allow students to answer this question in their private journals.

Media Wise

Gender Roles and Movies

People learn about gender roles by observing how other people behave. Family members, friends, and other adults may serve as roles models. People also receive messages about gender roles from movies. Use this checklist to evaluate how gender roles are shown in a movie.

Do the females tend to be less assertive than the males?	Yes	No
Are the male roles more action-oriented than the female roles?	Yes	No
Do the females share their feelings more easily than the males?	Yes	No
When there is a problem to solve, is the problem solver usually male?	Yes	No
Do the men tend to work outside the home and the women inside the home?	Yes	No

Two or more "Yes" answers indicate a movie that supports traditional gender roles.

Activity Use the checklist to evaluate gender roles in two movies. Then write a paragraph about what you observed. How do you think these movies affect people's opinions about gender roles? **WRITING**

Dating Concerns

Dating can be a stressful experience, even for adults. People often feel both excitement and anxiety before and during a date. They want to make a good impression. They worry about doing or saying the wrong thing. Teens often have an added concern—their family's expectations. **There are ways to make the dating experience less stressful. You can be yourself, communicate honestly, learn to handle rejection, and address your family's concerns.**

Be Yourself People often say that the best approach in social situations is to "be yourself." This is good advice because it takes energy to put on an act, and it is hard to keep up an act over time. Being yourself does not mean doing whatever you want without any concern for others. It does mean, for example, that if you are shy, you do not have to try to be the center of attention. Or if you are cautious, you do not have to be daring in order to impress others.

If feelings of shyness or insecurity keep you from dating, focus on ways you can meet new people and build your confidence. Join a club, volunteer to help plan a school event, or sign up for a school trip.

Connect to Your Life What concerns do you have about dating?

TEENS Are Asking . . .

Q: I am 14 years old. My parents say I'm too young to date. What can I do to convince them that they are wrong?

A: Ask your parents to set aside time to talk about this issue. Encourage them to state their specific concerns, and work together to find ways to address these concerns. Be respectful and mature—no yelling, sarcasm, or whining. Watch your body language.

Here are some ways to address your parents' concerns. Arrange for your parents to meet the person you want to date. Invite him or her to share a meal with your family or to go on a family outing. Be honest and follow family rules, especially curfews. These actions will help you earn your parents' trust. Be willing to compromise. Offer to go out with a group, rather than as a couple.

Communicate Honestly Even the most confident teens can feel awkward or self-conscious on occasion. If both people know what to expect on a date, the experience is likely to be less awkward. Use the questions in Figure 2 to discuss your plans with your date.

If you are honest, you can avoid many misunderstandings. For example, suppose someone asks you to go hiking, which you don't normally do. Make sure the person knows that you haven't been hiking before and are concerned about being able to keep up. With this information, the person could plan a shorter or less challenging hike.

If a date doesn't work out as planned, don't overreact. Your date will be impressed if you show that you can cope with unexpected events.

Learn to Handle Rejection When you ask someone out, the person may say no. Or after a first date, a person may not agree to a second. Here are some tips for handling rejection.

- Don't let fear of rejection keep you from asking someone out.
- Don't let a no lead to self-doubt. The person may not be ready for a relationship or may not share your interests.
- Just because one person says *no* that doesn't mean that other people will not want to go out with you.

Address Your Family's Concerns Dating is often an area of conflict between teens and adults. Adults may fear that dating will lead to risky behaviors, such as drug use, sexual activity, and reckless driving. It helps if you can talk calmly with your family about their concerns. It also helps if you share the answers to the questions in Figure 2 with them.

Parents and guardians never stop worrying about their children. But their fears may decrease if you follow the rules, tell the truth about what you are doing, and let your family meet the people you date.

Tips for Dating

Before you go out, ask:
- Where are we going?
- How will we get there?
- Is anyone else going?
- What will it cost and who will pay?
- When will we be back?
- How can I be reached in an emergency?

FIGURE 2 You improve your chances of having a successful dating experience if you ask the right questions in advance.

Section 1 Review

Key Ideas and Vocabulary

1. What does the term **infatuation** mean?
2. List four things people can learn by dating.
3. What can you do to make the dating experience less stressful?
4. Why do adults worry when teens begin to date?

Critical Thinking

5. **Applying Concepts** Suppose someone you really like invites you to go rock climbing. The person doesn't know that you have a fear of heights. How should you handle this situation?
6. **Comparing and Contrasting** What are some differences between infatuation and dating?
7. **Predicting** Blanca's mother finds out that Blanca lied about where she went and who she was with on Saturday night. How might this lie affect Blanca's relationship with her mother?

Health at School

Honest Communication With three of your classmates, write a short skit that shows the importance of honest communication. Pick a situation where failing to ask questions, or telling a lie when answering a question, causes a misunderstanding. WRITING

L3 Active Learning

Have students pretend that they are a parent or guardian of a teen. Ask them to make a list of dating rules for a teenage son or daughter. Then have them present the rules to a partner and explain why they think the rules are important.

3. Assess

Evaluate

These assignments can help you assess students' mastery of the section content.

L3 Section 1 Review

Answers appear below.

L2 Reteach

Review the four strategies offered for making the dating experience less stressful by asking volunteers to explain why each strategy is important.

L4 Enrich

Health at School

Honest Communication You may want to brainstorm a list of possible situations as a class before students begin to work in small groups. You may want to extend the exercise to include situations involving peers that occur outside of school.

Section 1 Review

1. a feeling of intense attraction to another person.
2. You can learn about someone's interests, personality, abilities, and values.
3. be yourself, communicate honestly, learn to handle rejection, address your family's concerns
4. They fear dating will lead to drug use, sexual activity, and reckless driving.
5. *Sample answer:* I should tell the person about my fear of heights.
6. Infatuation is a one-sided, often unrealistic, relationship. A dating relationship is two-sided, with a realistic chance of growth.
7. *Sample answer:* The mother might lose trust in Blanca and reduce her freedom.

Section 2

Choosing Abstinence

Objectives
Before class begins, write the objectives on the board. Have students copy the objectives into their notebooks at the start of class.

1. Focus

Warm-Up **Health Stats**

After students complete the writing assignment, ask if any of the results of the survey surprised them. Then, ask volunteers to share their responses to the writing assignment with the class.

Section 2

Choosing Abstinence

Objectives
- ▶ **Identify** some risks of sexual intimacy.
- ▶ **Explain** why emotional intimacy is important in close relationships.
- ▶ **List** some skills that can help you choose abstinence.

Vocabulary
- **emotional intimacy**
- **abstinence**

Warm-Up

Health Stats Who has the most influence on a teen's decisions about sex? The graph shows how some teens responded to this question.

WRITING Which influences do you think would help teens to make healthy decisions about sex? Explain.

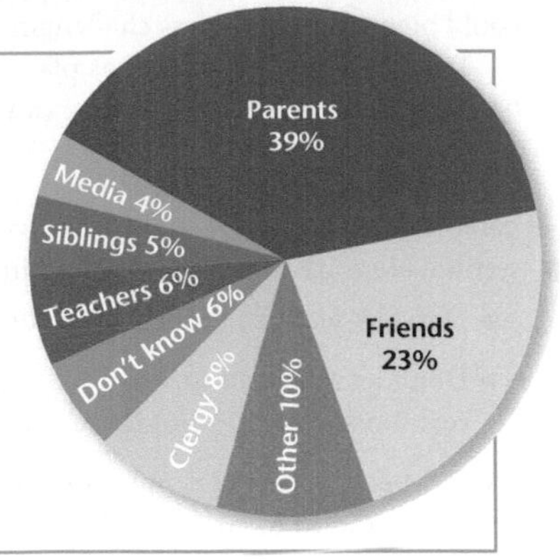

Risks of Sexual Intimacy

As teenagers become aware of their sexuality, some tough questions arise: How can I show affection without things going too far? Are my partner and I emotionally ready for a sexual relationship? There are no easy answers for such questions. It is important, however, to think about these questions before you have to make decisions that can affect the rest of your life.

As you think about sexual intimacy, there are some important issues for you to consider. **Sexual intimacy is not risk free. The risks include the effect on your emotional health, the effect on your relationship, the risk of pregnancy, and the risk of sexually transmitted infections.**

Effect on Your Emotional Health Decisions about sexual intimacy should be based on the values that you hold. Your family, friends, religion, culture, experiences, and the media help shape your values. Often the messages you receive from different sources will be contradictory. This makes it more difficult to sort out how you truly feel.

A decision to become sexually involved may go against a person's values. If the person makes the decision anyway, the person may feel guilty or ashamed. The person may feel that he or she has let down parents, friends, and others as well as himself or herself. The result of making snap decisions about sex is often a loss of self-respect. Using sex to prove something to oneself and others can also lower self-esteem.

Sensitive Issues
Even a general discussion on issues related to sexual decision making may be uncomfortable for some students. Keep the discussion focused on what typical teens might be likely to do in certain situations.

MATH and Health

L3 Graphing
Ask students to convert the information from the Warm-Up into a bar graph. The *x*-axis label should be "Influences on a Teen's Decisions About Sex"; the *y*-axis label should be "Percentage of Teens." Discuss how changing the format in which information is displayed can change the impact information has on a viewer. Ask students if they think the circle graph or the bar graph has more impact. Then ask how the impact might change if the data were presented in a paragraph.

Effect on Your Relationship A decision to become sexually intimate alters the way couples spend their time together. It also changes the way a couple relates to friends. Sexual intimacy can affect each person's expectations. One person may expect to have sex whenever the couple is together, while the other person may not. One person may become more possessive and put more demands on the other's time. One person may decide to end the relationship.

Often couples are not prepared for the complications that sexual intimacy adds to their relationship. Most couples find that these changes to their relationship are permanent. Although they may try, it is almost impossible to go back to the way things were before they had sex.

Risk of Pregnancy A teenage pregnancy can pose serious health problems for the baby and the mother. Babies born to young mothers are often smaller and less healthy than those born to older women. Teenage mothers are more likely to have health problems during pregnancy than women in their twenties. This is because pregnant teenagers do not always eat well or get adequate medical care during pregnancy, especially in the early months.

Besides health problems, what effect does a baby have on a teenage couple? Parents are legally responsible to care for their children. Teenage parents often report feeling overwhelmed and trapped. Many teenage mothers drop out of school. Some fathers don't help support or care for the child; others drop out of school and work at low-paying jobs.

Young people are aware of the problems teenage parents face, but they often don't think that pregnancy can happen to them. Few teens want to become pregnant. But one in six teenage girls who engage in sexual intercourse becomes pregnant. Sexual intimacy is a high-risk behavior for anyone who isn't ready to accept the responsibility of children.

Connect to Your Life **What effect might a pregnancy have on a teenage couple's relationship?**

FIGURE 3 After caring for a baby, a teenage mother may not have enough energy left for school.
Predicting How could dropping out of school affect the mother? How could it affect the baby?

About 25% of teen mothers have a second baby before age 20.

2. Teach

Risks of Sexual Intimacy

L3 Cooperative Learning

Have students work in small groups to list examples of physical contact that they would *not* classify as sexual intimacy. To help get the process started, write a few possible examples on the board, such as hugging, holding hands, or giving a back rub. After students are done, ask if it was difficult for groups to agree on all suggested examples. Also ask students to identify reasons for any disagreements.

L1 Visual Learning: Figure 3

Ask students to describe the photograph in Figure 3. Then, discuss what a mother has to do to take care of a baby and how these tasks could interfere with her ability to stay in school. Encourage students to suggest other typical teen activities that the mother might no longer be able to do.

Caption Answer *Sample answer:* If the mother drops out of school, she limits her job opportunities, her future income, and her ability to provide for her child.

L3 Cooperative Learning

Have students work in small groups to prepare a 60-second radio public service announcement aimed at teens. The goal is to encourage teens to think about the risks of sexual intimacy. If possible, have students record their announcements so they can play them for the class. **WRITING**

L4 Active Learning

Have students research the lifelong financial impact of becoming a teen parent. Students should find information that relates to both teen mothers and teen fathers. Ask students to use the results of their research to prepare a short lesson to share with the class.

Connect to Your Life *Sample answer:* A pregnancy could cause one or both partners to feel overwhelmed or trapped. These feelings would have a negative impact on the couple's relationship.

Differentiated Instruction

L1 Special Needs

Have students make a graphic organizer that outlines the four main risks of sexual intimacy. Tell students that they may use a concept map, a chart, or another format that clearly organizes the information. Provide students with models of graphic organizers before they begin. Some students may benefit from working in pairs. Have students add information to their organizer as they read.

Emotional Intimacy

L1 Class Discussion

Explain that one way you can tell that a couple has a close, emotionally intimate relationship is to observe how they behave. Write a few examples on the board—finishing each other's sentences, doing unexpected kind things, or sharing "inside" jokes. Challenge students to add additional items to the list. Then discuss how these behaviors can strengthen a relationship.

Abstinence Skills

L3 Building Health Skills

Analyzing Influences Have students make a list of their ten favorite songs about relationships. Then ask students to analyze the content of the songs. Do the words describe or encourage sexual activity? Is any of the language used demeaning to females? Are there any references to emotional intimacy? After students complete the activity, ask volunteers to share their findings. Then discuss what influence music might have on a teen's sexual behavior.

EL Building Vocabulary

Write the term *abstinence* on the board. Explain that the broad meaning of the term is the act of voluntarily doing without something a person views as pleasurable—sex, alcohol, cigarettes.

Risk of Sexually Transmitted Infections Some infections can be passed, or transmitted, from one person to another during sexual activity. These are called sexually transmitted infections, or STIs. If left untreated, many STIs cause serious health problems. For example, some STIs can cause infertility, or the inability to have children. Others shorten a person's life or require medical treatment throughout a person's life.

Emotional Intimacy

Contrary to what you may think, every teen is not sexually experienced. Millions of young people today choose to postpone sexual activity. On a television show, a young man spoke of his relationship with his girlfriend. "We're not ready for sex, but we share lots of other intimate experiences."

How can two people be intimate without being sexually involved? They can trust each other with personal feelings or dreams that they haven't told anyone else. They can exchange "inside" jokes. They can do kind things for each other and be best friends.

Emotional intimacy refers to the openness, sharing, affection, and trust that can develop in a close relationship. Two things can help a couple develop emotional intimacy. They must be honest with one another. They must be accepting and supportive of each other. **A couple can have a close relationship without being sexually intimate. But it is hard for them to keep a relationship close if there is no emotional intimacy.**

Abstinence Skills

Sergio and Selena met in class and became good friends. Soon, they started to date. As they spent more time together, they began to express their feelings of affection by hugging, kissing, and holding hands. Over time, the pressure to become more physically intimate grew stronger. But Sergio and Selena felt that abstinence was the best choice at this point in their lives.

Abstinence is the act of refraining from, or not having, sex. There are skills you can learn to help you choose abstinence when you are faced with the pressure to become more physically intimate. **These abstinence skills include setting clear limits, communicating your limits, avoiding high-pressure situations, and asserting yourself.**

FIGURE 4 Trust and affection are two signs of strong emotional bonds. These bonds form when couples are honest and supportive of one another.

WRITING and Health

L3 Persuasive E-mail

Ask students to write a persuasive e-mail to a fictional friend that uses information from the section to encourage the friend to choose abstinence. Remind students that the term *persuasive* means having the power to convince someone to believe or do something. Post students' completed letters in the classroom. Allow students to circulate and read the letters. Then ask students to point out characteristics of particularly effective letters.

FIGURE 5 It is important to discuss your limits on sexual intimacy as early as possible in a relationship. **Evaluating** Which communication skills are most important when you want to clearly state your limits?

Set Clear Limits It is natural to feel sexual attraction to someone you are dating. It is also natural to be unsure of how to handle these feelings. Most teenagers try to think ahead and set limits for expressing their sexual feelings. If you set limits before a situation arises, it will be easier to stick to the standards you set. Take some time now to set limits that you feel comfortable with. It is important to know your limits before you go out so you can avoid having to make a hasty decision.

To help yourself set limits, be sure to consider the important values that you hold and the possible consequences of your actions. It is essential that you make decisions with which you feel comfortable. Do not allow the expectations of friends, the media, and others to influence you to make decisions that may not be right for you.

Communicate Your Limits Once you have decided on your limits, it is important to communicate your feelings to your partner. Of course, it is best to discuss things as early as possible in a relationship. Do not wait until a situation arises in which your partner's expectations may be different from yours. It may be difficult to have an open, constructive discussion if you wait until that point to talk.

Try to talk honestly to your partner about your feelings and values. You may be surprised at how relieved your partner may be to hear how you feel. He or she may have been anxious about your expectations.

If you have been sexually involved, it doesn't mean that you have to continue to be sexually involved. You may decide that a relationship built around emotional intimacy makes more sense, and choose abstinence. If your partner tries to make you feel guilty, you may need to rethink your relationship. Do you really want to be with a person who does not respect your feelings or who does not value emotional intimacy?

Connect to Your Life **Are you comfortable talking with friends about your values? Why or why not?**

GO ONLINE
PearsonSuccessNet.com
For: More on abstinence

Visual Learning: Figure 5

Caption Answer *Sample answer:* Using "I" messages and assertiveness are most important when you want to clearly state your limits.

L3 Journal Writing

Remind students to consider their values when they make important decisions, such as setting limits for expression of sexual feelings. Ask students to write an entry in their private journals. In the entry, they should identify the personal values they can use to help them set limits for sexual activity. WRITING

L2 Cooperative Learning

Have pairs of students work together to make a list of "high-pressure" situations and "low-pressure" alternatives. For example, watching a rented movie as a couple when no one else is home versus going to a movie theater. Ask each group to share some responses with the class.

L3 Building Health Skills

Practicing Healthful Behaviors Have students work in small groups to practice refusal skills. Ask each group to make a list of ten things one person might say to convince another person to have sex. Then have the groups brainstorm a list of possible responses to each statement. Ask volunteers from each group to act out one statement and response. Remind students that tone of voice is key to the effective use of refusal skills.

Connect to Your Life Allow students to answer this question in their private journals.

L3 Content Update GO ONLINE

Visit Pearson SuccessNet to access more information about abstinence. Have students complete the Web activity.

Differentiated Instruction

L2 Less Proficient Readers

Have students work in small groups to develop an idea for a television public service announcement about how a person's intended message about limits might get misunderstood. Encourage students to use humor to make their point. Ask groups to present their ideas to the class. At minimum, the presentation should include a description of the situation and some dialogue. Some groups may want to use a storyboard with drawings to show the announcement frame by frame.

3. Assess

Evaluate

These assignments can help you assess students' mastery of the section content.

L3 Section 2 Review

Answers appear below.

L2 Reteach

Ask students to make a bulleted list of the risks that are associated with sexual intimacy. Then, have students write a one-sentence description of each abstinence skill.

L4 Enrich

Health at Home

Comparing Viewpoints If local papers don't have an advice column for teens, have students access syndicated teen advice columns online. After students complete the activity, ask them what they learned from doing the activity. For example, were their responses to the letters and those of the adults similar or different? Do they think the activity will make it possible for them to talk more openly in the future with an adult about sexual choices?

FIGURE 6 One way for couples to avoid high-pressure situations is to go out as a group.

Avoid High-Pressure Situations Sticking to the limits you set can be difficult. You can make it easier for yourself by avoiding certain situations. For example, if you are at an unsupervised party, you might feel pressured to have sex. But if you are in a public place, the temptation to engage in sexual activities is not as great. It is also important to avoid alcohol and other drugs, as they can blur your ability to think clearly.

Spend time with friends who share your values. You might want to include your date in family outings. Not only will you not be tempted to have sex, you will see how your date interacts with different people.

Assert Yourself If you find yourself in a situation where you are not comfortable with the level of physical intimacy, don't feel guilty about saying no. State clearly and directly that you want to stop. You may want to offer a reason, such as "I'm just not ready," so that the other person won't feel hurt or rejected.

At times, however, simply saying no once may not be effective. You may need to be firm and say something like "No! I said I don't want to do that." You may need to repeat yourself a few times before your partner realizes that you are serious. If necessary, get up and walk away.

One person may try to pressure another by saying that, at some levels of intimacy, it is impossible to stop without causing physical harm. This isn't true. The person might also say things like "If you loved me, you would do it," or "Everybody does it." Remember that you will respect yourself more for sticking to your limits than for giving in to pressure.

If your partner does not respect the limits you set, the relationship may not be worth continuing. Try to meet people who understand the importance of dealing responsibly with sexual feelings. Look for people who value emotional intimacy.

Section 2 Review

Key Ideas and Vocabulary

1. What are four possible risks of sexual intimacy?
2. Define **emotional intimacy.**
3. How can emotional intimacy help a relationship to grow?
4. What is **abstinence?** What skills can help you to choose abstinence?

Critical Thinking

5. **Making Judgments** Review the risks of sexual intimacy. Which risk would be most likely to keep you from being sexually intimate? Give a reason for your choice.

Health at Home

Comparing Viewpoints Work with a parent or another trusted adult. Select two letters about teenage sexual choices from an advice column in a newspaper. Separately, the two of you should write responses to the letters. Then compare your responses to each other's and to the actual advice offered in the newspaper. **WRITING**

6. **Applying Concepts** How could a person who doesn't want to be sexually involved respond to each of these "pressure" lines?
   a. "If you loved me, you would have sex with me."
   b. "Everyone else is having sex. What's wrong with you?"
   c. "You know you want to. Everyone wants to."

Section 2 Review

1. the effects on your emotional health and relationship, the risks of pregnancy and STIs
2. the openness, sharing, affection, and trust that can develop in a close relationship
3. It helps keep a relationship close.
4. the act of refraining from sexual intimacy; setting clear limits, communicating your limits, avoiding high-pressure situations, and asserting yourself
5. *Sample answer:* the risk of pregnancy, because becoming a parent would prevent me from focusing on my education
6. a. *Sample answer:* If you loved me, you would respect my values.
   b. *Sample answer:* There's nothing wrong with me. Many teens choose not to have sex.
   c. *Sample answer:* I don't have to do everything I may want to do.

Unhealthy Relationships

Warm-Up

Myth **A person who is raped is usually attacked by a stranger.**

Fact **Most victims of rape know their attackers.**

WRITING What precautions could someone take to reduce the risk of being raped by a friend or acquaintance?

Section 3

Objectives

- **Describe** the cycle of violence.
- **Identify** reasons why a person should report a rape.
- **Explain** the effect of sexual abuse on a victim.
- **Describe** an effective way to reduce sexual harassment at school.

Vocabulary

- dating violence
- physical abuse
- emotional abuse
- sexual abuse
- rape
- date rape
- statutory rape
- incest
- pedophilia
- sexual harassment

Violence in Dating Relationships

Unfortunately, some teen relationships turn violent. One partner may slap the other when he or she is angry. Or make fun of the other's looks or abilities. Or constantly check up to find out what the person is doing. These are examples of dating violence. **Dating violence** is a pattern of physical, emotional, or sexual abuse that occurs in a dating relationship.

- **Physical Abuse** Intentionally causing physical harm to another person is called **physical abuse.** A person who has frequent bruises may say "I tripped" or "I walked into a door." A more likely explanation is that he or she is a victim of physical abuse.
- **Emotional Abuse** "You never do anything right." "Without me, you're nothing." A person who constantly hears negative statements like these is likely to suffer from emotional abuse. **Emotional abuse** is the nonphysical mistreatment of a person. Emotional abuse does not leave visible scars. But it does leave victims feeling inadequate, helpless, or worthless. They may also feel anxious or depressed.
- **Sexual Abuse** When one person forces another to engage in any unwanted sexual behavior, the person is committing **sexual abuse.** The abuser may use physical force to get the victim to cooperate. He or she may also use threats or bribes.

Section 3

Unhealthy Relationships

Objectives
Before class begins, write the objectives on the board. Have students copy the objectives into their notebooks at the start of class.

1. Focus

Warm-Up Myth/Fact

Have a class discussion of the myth about rape before students begin their writing. Challenge students to identify specific precautions. Ask volunteers to share their responses with the class.

2. Teach

Violence in Dating Relationships

L3 Class Discussion

Challenge students to complete the phrase "Sticks and stones can break my bones…" *(but names will never hurt me).* Ask students if they think this saying is true or false. Encourage students to revise this phrase to accurately reflect the damage that can be inflicted by emotional abuse. Have volunteers share their revised saying with the class.

Differentiated Instruction

L2 Less Proficient Readers

Ask students to fold a piece of notebook paper in thirds to create three vertical columns. Have students label the three columns *Physical Abuse, Sexual Abuse,* and *Emotional Abuse.* Encourage students to add information about various forms of abuse to the correct columns as they read.

When students have completed their reading, have them review their notes. For each form of abuse, have students check to see that they recorded the main idea and several details. Explain that the organizer can be used as a study aid as they prepare for the section review and the chapter review.

L3 Visual Learning: Figure 7

Image Bank Figure 6-9

Have students read the description of each stage in the cycle of violence. Ask: **How is a victim likely to respond during the tension-building stage?** *(The victim may adjust his or her behavior in an attempt to please the abuser and avoid a violent episode.)* **What explanation can you offer for the abuser's actions during the calm stage?** *(Sample answer: The abuser is trying to maintain control, make the victim feel responsible, or keep the victim from seeking help.)*

Caption Answer *Sample answer:* Victims may think they can control the cycle through their behavior, but abusers are always responsible for the violence.

L1 Cooperative learning

Have students work together to make posters about the warning signs of abuse. If students are unclear about a warning sign, provide one or two examples. Encourage students to use drawings as well as words.

L3 Building Health Skills

Advocacy Divide the class into small groups. Have each group develop a plan for advocating for a friend who is in a violent relationship. Then ask the groups to share their plans with the class. Challenge students to identify strategies that they feel would be most effective, and to provide reasons for their choices. Emphasize that notifying a trusted adult is important in all situations involving violence.

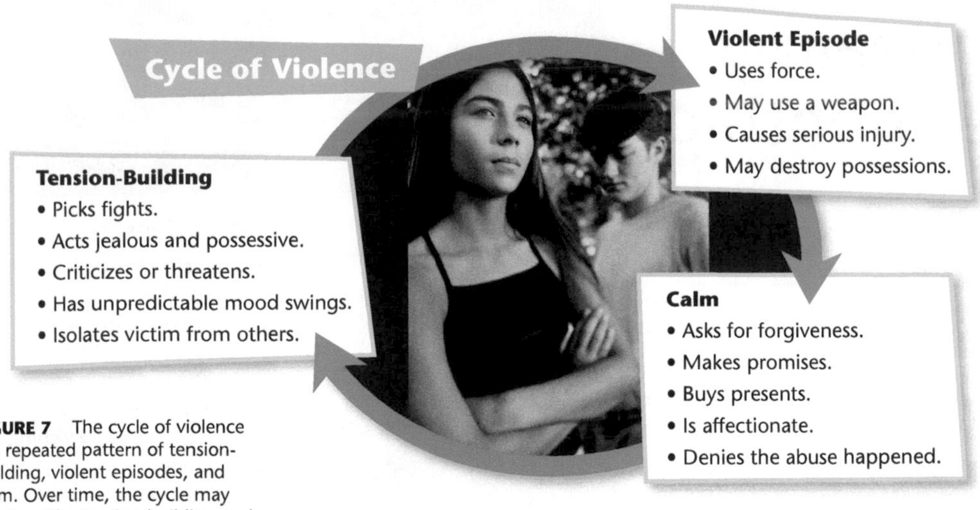

FIGURE 7 The cycle of violence is a repeated pattern of tension-building, violent episodes, and calm. Over time, the cycle may shorten. The tension-building and calm stages may disappear, leaving only a series of violent episodes. **Predicting** What control does the victim have over the cycle of violence?

The Cycle of Violence Often abuse occurs as part of the three-stage cycle in Figure 7. **The cycle of violence consists of a tension-building stage, a violent episode, and a calm or "honeymoon" stage.** During the tension-building stage, the victim may try to please the abuser or reason with the abuser in order to prevent violence. Sometimes victims describe this stage as "walking on eggshells." The tension is broken by a violent episode.

During the calm stage, the abuser may apologize and promise to never abuse the victim again. The abuser may also blame the victim for the abuse. The calm is followed by another tension-building stage.

The Need for Control Why would a person abuse someone that he or she claims to care about? Experts agree that the major reason people abuse others is the need for control. Odd as it may seem, abusers tend to see themselves as victims. They think that they have the right to control an intimate relationship. Being able to control another person makes them feel powerful.

Warning Signs of Abuse A good way to avoid the cycle of violence is to recognize the warning signs that can lead to abuse.

- Your date is jealous when you talk to others.
- Your date makes all the decisions and tries to control what you do.
- Your date has a history of bad relationships.
- You feel isolated from your friends and family.
- You feel less self-confident when you are with your date.
- You change how you behave to avoid an argument.

WRITING and Health

L3 Dialogue

Have students consider the situation when a teen notices signs that a friend is in a violent dating relationship. Have students write a dialogue that the concerned friend might have with the abused friend. Ask students to consider how to best approach the topic. Have them consider how the abused friend might respond. Will the friend deny that the relationship is violent, or say that he or she is responsible for the behavior?

Ending the Abuse Why would a teen remain in an abusive relationship or hide the abuse from others? Some teens may view a possessive or jealous partner as romantic. Or they may think the behavior is normal because friends are in similar relationships. Females may think that males are supposed to act in a controlling manner or that physical aggression is a sign of masculinity. Males may be ashamed to admit that they are being abused for fear of being seen as weak. Sadly, some teens may think that they deserve to be abused. Others may fear being alone.

The first step to ending an abusive relationship is to admit that the abuse exists. The second step is to realize that you are not to blame for the abuse and that you cannot change how your abuser behaves. Seek the support of friends and family. Call an abuse hotline if you want anonymous advice. Talk to a counselor, teacher, doctor, or social worker, but be aware that these adults are legally required to report abuse.

Rape

When one person forces another to have sex, the act is called **rape.** Although rape is a problem for both females and males, the majority of victims are female.

Date Rape Most women who are raped know the person who raped them. The person may have been an acquaintance, a casual date, or a steady date. Rape that occurs during a date is often called **date rape.**

The rapist may have used a "date rape drug." These fast-acting drugs are hard to detect in food or a drink because they are colorless, tasteless, and odorless. Later, the victim will feel "hung over" and be unable to recall the rape. Friends will say that the victim acted drunk. It is important to do what you can to decrease your chances of being raped by a date or acquaintance. Figure 8 lists some tips for dating safely.

Statutory Rape Date rape is a crime. So is having sex with someone the state considers too young to give his or her consent. Having sex with someone who is under the age of consent is called **statutory rape.** The age of consent varies among states, from age 14 to age 18. A state is more likely to charge a person with rape when the age difference is greater than three years.

Reporting Rape Some people don't report rapes, especially date rapes. They may be ashamed, feel responsible, or think they won't be believed. **But reporting a rape is important so the victim can receive medical attention and counseling. Also, law enforcement can collect evidence needed to prosecute the rapist and prevent future rapes.** A person who is raped should contact the police or a rape crisis center. Either group can arrange for the person to see a doctor or nurse. A counselor can discuss the risks of STIs and offer females a drug to prevent a possible pregnancy.

Tips for Dating Safely

- Go out as a group.
- Let someone know where you are going.
- Avoid alcohol or other drugs.
- Have money to get home.
- In an emergency, call 911.

FIGURE 8 These tips can help decrease the chances of date rape.

Rape

L3 Addressing Misconceptions

Reason for Rapes Some people think that women who have been raped "asked" for it in some way. For example, people may comment on the clothes a woman was wearing or how she was flirting with her assailant. Emphasize that no one "asks" to be raped, and that a victim's appearance, behavior, or history should not be used to excuse a rapist.

L1 Visual Learning Figure 8

Students may have trouble reconciling the instruction to not blame the victim with the instruction to take precautions to avoid being raped. Explain that a person takes precautions to reduce the risk of a certain outcome. Then have volunteers explain how each tip listed in Figure 8 could decrease the chances of a date rape occurring.

EL Building Vocabulary

Explain that the term *statutory* is an example of an adjective formed from a noun by adding a suffix. In this case the suffice is *–ory* and the noun is *statute*. A statute is a formal regulation or law.

Differentiated Instruction

L4 Gifted and Talented

Have interested students interview a person who works at a rape crisis center. Ask students to prepare questions in advance. Suggest that students focus on what happens to a person who reports a rape. Students may also want to ask about the roles of health professionals and law enforcement after a rape is reported. Students should use what they learn to prepare a presentation for the class.

Sexual Abuse of Children

L2 Visual Learning: Figure 9

Have students look at Figure 9. Ask: **How is this poster an example of advocacy?** *(The poster draws attention to the problem of child abuse and encourages people to help stop the abuse.)* Discuss how an image often can be more powerful than words when you want to convey a message.

Caption Answer *Sample answer:* The poster is aimed at adults because they are responsible for protecting children.

L3 Class Discussion

Remind students that child abuse is never the child's fault. Emphasize that abuse should not be kept a secret, but should be reported to a trusted adult. Explain that abuse can also be reported to the National Child Abuse hotline (1-800-422-4453 or 1-800-4-A-CHILD). Tell students this is a free telephone call, and the hotline is available 24 hours a day, 7 days a week.

Connect to Your Life Allow students to answer this question in their private journals.

Sexual Harassment

L3 Building Health Skills

Communicating Describe this scenario to students: Each day, a female student takes the bus to school. An older male student rides the same bus. Almost every day, the male student makes some remark about the female's body. Sometimes he "accidentally" brushes against the female student as she walks down the aisle. Have students work in pairs to write a role-play that shows how the female student could communicate her displeasure to the male student or to school authorities. Call on pairs to perform their role-play for the class. Discuss which strategies might be most effective. **WRITING**

Figure 9 This poster is advocating against the sexual abuse of children.
Predicting Who do you think is the intended audience for this poster?

Sexual Abuse of Children

Accurate data on how many children and adolescents are victims of sexual abuse by adults are hard to find. Many cases are not reported. Typically, the adult is someone the victim knows well. The adult may be a parent, stepparent, older sibling, other relative, or a family friend.

Incest Sex between people who are too closely related to marry legally is called **incest.** Incest is a crime in all states, but the definition varies. All states consider sex between family members who are biologically related to be incest. Some states also define incest to include relationships based on adoption or remarriage. Whatever the legal definition, sexual behavior that feels wrong *is* wrong. The victim of the abuse should seek help.

Pedophilia Sometimes children are abused by a person with a mental disorder called pedophilia. People with **pedophilia** (ped uh FIL ee uh) have a sexual attraction to children. These people are known as pedophiles, or child molesters. They are almost always male. Some abuse family members. Others abuse children who are not related to them.

Ending the Abuse Even a single instance of sexual abuse can have a devastating effect. The victim feels guilty and ashamed. **In the victim's mind, he or she assumes all the responsibility or blame for the event.** It becomes difficult for the victim to trust others and develop caring relationships. Victims often experience symptoms of post-traumatic stress disorder, such as flashbacks and nightmares.

Victims of sexual abuse should talk with a trusted adult or call the Child Abuse Hotline. Deciding to seek help may be difficult. Victims risk angering, hurting, or betraying the abuser. If the abuser is a family member, sometimes other relatives don't want to believe what is going on and may accuse the victim of lying. The abuser may threaten the child to keep the child from telling. But it is more dangerous to believe the abuser's threats than to report the abuse. Remember, no one has the right to abuse you.

Connect to Your Life **What would you do if you knew a friend was being abused?**

Differentiated Instruction

L4 Gifted and Talented

Grassroots organizations have been trying since the late 1990s to get states to close "incest loopholes." This term refers to the practice of imposing less severe penalties for child sexual abuse that occurs within families as compared to child sexual abuse by strangers. The campaigns have been successful in some states.

Ask interested students to research the laws in your state to find out how incest is defined and if an "incest loophole" exists. In addition to searching online, students may want to contact a police officer, a prosecutor, or a member of the state legislature. Ask students to share their findings with the class.

Sexual Harassment

Mariah's friend, Eduardo, told her that there were some explicit sexual comments about her in the boy's bathroom. She didn't pay much attention until a student she didn't know asked her for a sexual favor. What Maria experienced was sexual harassment.

Sexual harassment is any uninvited and unwelcome sexual remark or sexual advance. Making comments about a person's body parts is an example. So is unwanted touching or spreading rumors about someone's sexual behavior. Telling crude jokes in study hall is also an example. The jokes may make some students uncomfortable.

Sadly, sometimes the person doing the harassing is an adult. The difference in power between the adult and the student makes the behavior even less acceptable. **If school administrators, teachers, and students work together, they can stop sexual harassment.**

What Schools Must Do Sexual harassment in schools is illegal. The administration at a school is required by law to respond quickly and forcefully when students complain about sexual harassment. If the school doesn't act, and the harassment continues, the victim has grounds to sue the harasser and the school.

What You Can Do Here are ways you can stop sexual harassment.

- Speak up assertively when you feel disrespected.
- Use your refusal skills to reject unwanted sexual advances.
- Avoid having to be alone with someone you don't trust.
- Report behavior that you think is sexual harassment to an adult.

GO ONLINE
PearsonSuccessNet.com
For: More on dating responsibly

Section 3 Review

Key Ideas and Vocabulary

1. What is **dating violence?**
2. Describe the cycle of violence that can occur in a relationship.
3. Why should a person report a rape?
4. How does sexual abuse affect a victim?
5. What is **sexual harassment?** What is an effective way to stop sexual harassment at school?

Critical Thinking

6. **Comparing and Contrasting** What do physical abuse and emotional abuse have in common?
7. **Applying Concepts** Why would an abuser want to isolate a victim from family and friends?

Health and Community

Help Combat Dating Violence Find out about volunteer organizations in your community that deal with dating violence. For example, you could baby-sit for children at a local women's shelter. Or invite a police officer to talk about dating violence at a school assembly. Then write a paragraph summarizing what you learned. WRITING

8. **Evaluating** When Tamara's friends complain about how Dillon treats Tamara, she usually makes excuses for him. She says that he is under a lot of pressure and that her behavior often angers him. What advice would you give Tamara about her relationship with Dillon? WRITING

L1 Class Discussion

Explain that people sometimes disagree on what actions to classify as sexual harassment. The key is knowing how the potential "victim" feels. For example, one young woman may be flattered to have young men stare at her while another might be uncomfortable. Discuss ways that people can respond if words or actions make them uncomfortable.

L3 Content Update GO ONLINE

Visit Pearson SuccessNet to access more information about dating responsibly. Have students complete the Web activity.

3. Assess

Evaluate

These assignments can help you assess students' mastery of the section content.

L3 Section 3 Review

Answers appear below.

L2 Reteach

Have students work in pairs to review the boldface headings in the section. For each heading, ask students to discuss the main ideas and vocabulary.

L4 Enrich

Health and Community

Help Combat Dating Violence Help the class brainstorm a list of activities that students could do to help combat dating violence. After students complete their writing, discuss what they learned. Ask students to identify any new or surprising facts that they learned about dating violence.

Section 3 Review

1. a pattern of emotional, physical, or sexual abuse that occurs in a dating relationship
2. There is a period of tension building, a violent episode, and a period of calm.
3. so the victim can receive medical attention and counseling and law enforcement can collect evidence
4. The victim assumes all the responsibility and blame for the event.
5. any unwanted and unwelcome sexual remark or sexual advance; administrators, teachers, and students must work together
6. *Sample answer:* The victim suffers and the abuse is likely to be repeated.
7. *Sample answer:* A victim who is isolated is easier to control because he or she lacks a support system.
8. Answers should note that Tamara isn't responsible for Dillon's behavior.

Section 4

Sexual Issues in Society

Objectives
Before class begins, write the objectives on the board. Have students copy the objectives into their notebooks at the start of class.

1. Focus

***Warm-Up* Advice Line**

After students finish writing, use a show of hands to find out how many students would advise the young woman to take the trip and how many would not. Ask volunteers to provide reasons for their decisions. Use student responses to introduce the topic of Internet safety.

Section 4

Sexual Issues in Society

Objectives
- **List** three rules to follow to use the Internet safely.
- **Describe** two industries that profit from sexual exploitation.

Vocabulary
- prostitution
- pornography

Warm-Up

Dear Advice Line,

I really like this guy I met in a chat room. He and I share so many interests. Lately he has been asking me to come and meet him in person. I have enough money for the bus trip from my town to his.

WRITING What advice would you give this person?

Internet Safety

You probably know some basic rules for avoiding abuse by a stranger. When you are home alone, keep the doors locked and don't open the door for a stranger. Never let a caller know you are home alone. Avoid dark or deserted places. Keep your doors locked when driving and park in a well-lit place. Do not hitchhike or pick up a hitchhiker.

There is a similar list of rules you should know to protect yourself when you use the Internet. **Keep your identity private, be wary of people you meet online, and don't respond to inappropriate messages.** By following these rules, you can reduce the risks of using the Internet while enjoying the benefits.

Keep Your Identity Private A Web site may ask you for information about yourself before letting you access the site. It may ask for your mailing address, phone number, age, and gender. You may be offered a free gift or a chance to enter a contest. Be cautious. The site may not be what it appears to be. The person who set up the site may be looking for someone to harm. The more personal the questions, the more cautious you should be. Be even more cautious if the site has sexual content.

Some teens have their own Web sites. Most teens post material on other people's Web sites. When you post something on the Web, never include your home address, telephone number, or a photograph. Also remember that any information you send to one person in an e-mail, including photographs, can easily be forwarded to many people.

TEENS *Are Asking . . .*

Q: I enjoy being able to chat with people online more than I enjoy talking with people face to face. I find it easier to open up online. Does this behavior seem odd?

A: No. Some people, especially those who are shy, find it easier to communicate with others electronically. In time, your success with electronic communication may make you more confident about your ability to converse in person. You do need to consider what you mean by "open up." If you mean express your opinions, that's fine, but be cautious about sharing personal information that could be used to identify you or your family.

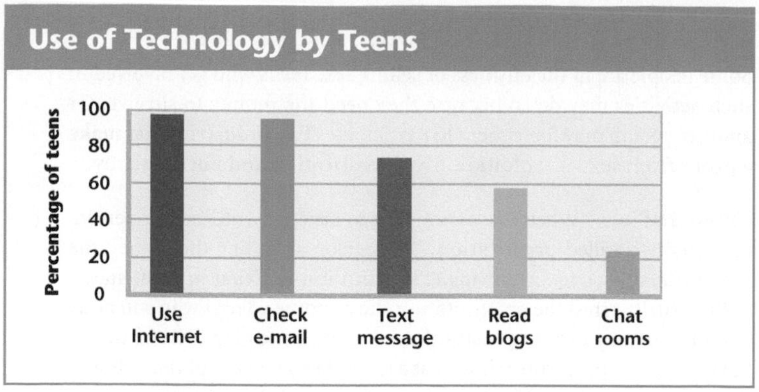

FIGURE 10 Teens were surveyed about which technologies they used at least once a week. The results show why it is important for teens to know how to use the Internet safely. **Calculating** Based on the graph, how many students in a class of 30 students are likely to read blogs? MATH

Be Wary of People You Meet Online Chatting online with others who share your interests can be fun. You might even learn something. But there are risks. To protect yourself, remember not to share information that could be used to identify you. Avoid saying things you would not say if you were face to face with a group of people. Leave a chat room if people begin to talk about a topic that makes you feel uncomfortable.

Over time you may start to think of people you chat with regularly as friends. However, you don't know who these "friends" really are. Online, it is easy for a person to pretend to be a teen when he or she is really an adult. The person may also pretend to share your interests to attract your attention in hopes of taking advantage of you.

Ideally, you should never agree to meet with someone you chat with online. If you do decide to arrange a meeting, follow these rules. Someone who is telling the truth will understand your concerns.

- Always discuss your plans with a parent or guardian.
- Never go to a meeting by yourself.
- Arrange to meet in a public place that you are familiar with.

Don't Respond to Inappropriate Messages People who use the Internet often receive e-mails from people they do not know. Most are messages from people who are trying to sell a product or service. If you respond to these e-mails, the amount of unwanted e-mails, or "spam," that you receive is likely to multiply.

Sometimes people use e-mails, text messages, or chat rooms to threaten, or harass, other people. This behavior is called cyber bullying. If you get such a message, don't respond. If you continue to receive similar messages, show them to a parent or other trusted adult. Your Internet provider may be able to identify the source. Report any material that seems illegal to law enforcement. Examples include threats to your safety, threats against others, and sexually explicit images of children.

Connect to Your Life **What are two specific actions you could take to increase your Internet safety?**

2. Teach

Internet Safety

L3 Visual Learning Figure 10

Have students do a survey to find out how technology use among students at your school compares with the data in Figure 10. Divide the project into tasks and have students work in small groups to complete the tasks. One group could prepare the questionnaire. A second group could figure out the best way to collect the data. A third group could tabulate and graph the results.
Caption Answer 17 students

L2 Building Health Skills

Advocacy Have students work with a partner to create a 30-second public service announcement about Internet safety. Encourage students to think of a slogan to use in their PSA. Point out that a 30-second announcement is brief, perhaps 30 to 40 words. A good PSA often has even fewer words, allowing time for pauses and music. Students should select music that is appropriate for the message. Ask students to record and play their announcements for the class.

L3 Building Media Literacy

Have interested students check Web sites that teens typically use to see what protections, if any, these sites provide. For example, does the site have an age limit? Does the site warn users about the risks of sharing information online? Are users able to limit access to their postings?

Connect to Your Life *Sample answer:* I can avoid Web sites with sexually explicit content. If I receive inappropriate messages, I can show them to a trusted adult.

Differentiated Instruction

EL English Language Learners

Pair English Language learners with more fluent classmates. Have each pair identify terms in the section that are unfamiliar to the English Language learner. Then, ask the pairs to discuss and define each term.

You could extend the activity by having the pairs discuss the availability of Web sites in languages other than English. Are there sites that are parallel in function to the sites available to English speakers?

Chapter 3, Section 4

Prostitution and Pornography

L3 Cooperative Learning

Have students work in small groups to make a list of alternatives to running away. Then, compile a list of alternatives on the board. Ask students to suggest reasons why teens might run away from home. For each reason, identify one or two appropriate alternatives.

L3 Class Discussion

Discuss the use of filters to block access to certain types of online information or specific Web sites. Ask students if they understand why adults might want to restrict their access to certain sites. Have them list some benefits and drawbacks of filters. For example, do some filters exclude more content than is intended?

3. Assess

Evaluate

These assignments can help you assess students' mastery of the section content.

L3 Section 2 Review

Answers appear below.

L2 Reteach

Ask students to write fill-in-the-blank questions based on the information in the section. Then, have pairs of students exchange and answer each other's questions.

L4 Enrich

Health at Home

Comparing Viewpoints Students may not have access to the Web at home or they may not have access to social networking sites. Either print out a few profiles for students to use or ask students to have a general discussion with a parent or guardian about Internet use. Ask volunteers to share their results with the class.

One-third of teens on the street are lured into prostitution within 48 hours.

FIGURE 11 Runaways are easy targets for people involved in pornography and prostitution.

Prostitution and Pornography

Some people are in the business of selling sex. Teens who get involved in such activities may do so because they need the money to survive. Or another person may force them to participate. **Two industries that make a profit from sexual exploitation are prostitution and pornography.**

Prostitution When one person pays to have sex with another person, the activity is called **prostitution.** The person accepting the money, the prostitute, can be female or male. Prostitution is illegal in most states. Police usually arrest the prostitute, not the customer. Teens who run away from home may turn to prostitution to earn money for food or drugs. Surveys of teen prostitutes show that around forty percent of the girls and thirty percent of the boys were victims of sexual abuse at home.

A pimp is a person who finds clients for prostitutes. The pimp keeps most of the money the prostitute earns. Pimps target teenage runaways by pretending to be their friend. Frequently, the pimp uses drugs and physical violence to control a prostitute.

Pornography Images and words that are designed to excite sexual arousal are called **pornography.** Pornography is difficult to define. But people tend to say that they know it when they see it. Everyone agrees that the use of children in pornography is exploitation. Making and distributing child pornography is also illegal.

Runaways may agree to make pornography because they are desperate for money. Other teens are lured by false promises of a modeling or acting career. Be suspicious of strangers who offer to take photographs of you for free. Also, don't let a friend talk you into posing for nude photographs or making a sexually explicit video. Think about what could happen to those images later on. They might end up on a Web site.

Section 4 Review

Key Ideas and Vocabulary

1. What are three things you can do to protect yourself when you use the Internet?
2. Name two industries that make a profit from sexual exploitation.
3. Define **prostitution**.
4. What is **pornography**?

Critical Thinking

5. **Relating Cause and Effect** How could abuse within a family contribute to the problem of runaways?

Health at Home

Comparing Viewpoints Work with a parent or another trusted adult. Look at some profiles that teens have posted on a social networking Web site. Discuss your opinions of the profiles. Then write a paragraph summarizing the discussion, noting areas of agreement and areas of disagreement. WRITING

6. **Applying Concepts** Someone calls you at home and asks you to take a phone survey. Which rules about Internet safety would apply in this situation? Explain your answer.

Section 4 Review

1. Keep your identity private, be wary of people you meet online, and don't respond to inappropriate messages.
2. prostitution and pornography
3. when one person pays to have sex with another person
4. images and words that are designed to excite sexual arousal
5. *Sample answer:* A child who is abused may decide to run away to avoid further abuse.
6. Students could reasonably argue that all the rules apply. For example, they should not share personal information about themselves or their families.

56 Chapter 3

Chapter 3 Review

VIDEO **TEENS Talk**

Choosing Abstinence Describe three things you learned from the video about the benefits of choosing abstinence.

Reviewing Key Ideas

Section 1

1. An infatuation is characterized by
   a. intense physical attraction.
   b. honest communication.
   c. shared interests and values.
   d. mutual trust and acceptance.
2. What are some benefits of steady dating? What are some drawbacks?
3. What are three things you can do to help address your family's concerns about dating?
4. **Critical Thinking** Three weeks in a row you invite someone you like to go to the movies. Each time the person says "I would like to go, but I have other plans." Should you try again? Why or why not?

Section 2

5. The act of refraining from sex is called
   a. sexual intimacy.
   b. emotional intimacy.
   c. abstinence.
   d. sexual involvement.
6. In what ways does having a baby change the lives of teenage parents?
7. Describe two things a couple could do to increase their emotional intimacy.
8. Explain why it is important to think about your limits before you are faced with a decision about sexual intimacy.
9. **Critical Thinking** Jada's communication style is passive. How could this style lead to misunderstandings about sexual intimacy?

Section 3

10. The nonphysical mistreatment of a person is
    a. physical abuse.
    b. sexual abuse.
    c. emotional abuse.
    d. statutory rape.
11. List at least four reasons why a teen might remain in an abusive relationship.
12. What should a student do when faced with sexual harassment at school?
13. **Critical Thinking** Why is it as important to address emotional abuse as it is to deal with physical abuse?
14. **Critical Thinking** Why do you think that a child who is abused by an adult might feel responsible for the abuse?

Section 4

15. Why is it important to protect your identity when you use the Internet?
16. What should you do if you receive e-mails that contain threats?
17. **Critical Thinking** Besides being arrested, what risks do prostitutes face?
18. **Critical Thinking** What could a person who wants to run away from home do instead?

Building Health Skills

19. **Making Decisions** Develop a list of rules to follow in a dating relationship. Make sure your rules emphasize respect for yourself and others.
20. **Setting Goals** Choose one of the abstinence skills you studied in Section 2. Make an action plan to apply this skill to situations other than choosing abstinence. For example, you could set clear limits not to be interrupted when you are doing your homework. Monitor your progress and adjust your action plan, if necessary. **WRITING**
21. **Advocacy** A friend who wants to be a model has been posing for suggestive photographs. What advice would you give your friend?

Health and Community

Community Guide for Teens Design a guide for teens who are new to your community. Describe things they can do to meet people. Include all the necessary details about the activities, such as times, dress codes, and costs. You may want to include a map with locations marked. **WRITING**

Chapter 3 Review

Reviewing Key Ideas

Section 1

1. a
2. Benefits: security and getting to know one person well; drawbacks: limits chance of meeting others, increased pressure to take part in sexual activity
3. Follow the rules, tell the truth about what you are doing, and let your family meet the people you date.
4. *Sample answer:* I would try again if the person clearly expressed an interest in spending time together.

Section 2

5. c
6. Parents feel trapped and overwhelmed.
7. *Sample answer:* do kind things for each other and share feelings
8. Setting limits in advance helps you avoid making a hasty decision later.
9. *Sample answer:* Jada may not be able to clearly communicate her limits.

Section 3

10. c
11. view the abuse as romantic, think abuse is normal, fear being alone, or think the abuse is deserved
12. Speak up assertively, use refusal skills to reject sexual advances, avoid being alone with the person, and report the behavior to an adult.
13. Emotional abuse leaves victims feeling helpless or worthless.
14. *Sample answer:* If an adult tells a child that his or her behavior has caused the abuse, the child is likely to believe the adult.

Section 4

15. *Sample answer:* Someone could use the information to harm you.
16. Don't respond. If you continue to receive similar e-mails, tell an adult.
17. *Sample answer:* He or she is at risk for physical abuse or STIs.
18. *Sample answer:* Confide in a trusted relative, neighbor, member of the clergy, or school counselor.

Health and Community

Community Guide for Teens Have students work in groups to make a list of things to do. Group members could cooperate to research the necessary details, write the copy, and produce the guide. Alternatively, interested students could work together to produce a guide that the school could give to new students.

Building Health Skills

19. The rules should show an understanding of the meaning of *respect*, and an awareness of the warning signs of abuse.
20. Let students keep their plans private.
21. *Sample answer:* I would express my concern about how the photos might be used now or in the future.

CHAPTER 4

Chapter Preview

Section 1 Marriage and Family Decisions
Marriage is part of many adults' lives, and many factors influence a marriage's success. Couples must weigh many factors when deciding whether to have children.

Section 2 Development Before Birth
Immediately after fertilization, the fertilized egg undergoes many cell divisions as it travels to the uterus. After the embryo implants in the uterus, the amniotic sac, placenta, and umbilical cord develop and protect and nourish the embryo. From the start of the third month of pregnancy, the embryo is known as a fetus.

Section 3 Pregnancy
Getting proper nutrition and exercise and avoiding drugs and environmental hazards are especially important before and during pregnancy. Regular doctor visits throughout pregnancy help ensure the birth of a healthy baby. Teen pregnancies are especially susceptible to complications.

Section 4 Preventing Pregnancy
There are numerous ways of preventing pregnancy, including abstinence and various types of contraception.

National Health Education Standards Correlation

1.12.5, 1.12.8, 2.12.8, 3.12.1, 3.12.2, 3.12.3, 3.12.4, 5.12.2, 7.12.1, 7.12.2, 7.12.3

CHAPTER 4

Planning for the Future

1 Marriage and Family Decisions
2 Development Before Birth
3 Pregnancy
- **Hands-On Activity** Be a Parent for a Day

4 Preventing Pregnancy

GO ONLINE PearsonSuccessNet.com

VIDEO 19

TEENS Talk

Teen Pregnancy

Preview **Activity**

How Would Your Plans Change?

Complete this activity before you watch the video.

1. Make a list of your plans for the weekend. Make a second list of your plans for after graduation.
2. Now suppose that you were a teen parent. Describe all the ways you think your weekend plans and your long-term plans would need to change. **WRITING**

58

GO ONLINE
PearsonSuccessNet.com
For resources and activities for this chapter.

Sensitive Issues

- Many students may feel uncomfortable during discussions of pregnancy because of the association with sexual activity and the intimate involvement with female anatomy. To help students feel comfortable, maintain a matter-of-fact tone in all discussions about these concepts.
- Keep in mind that some students in the class may be or have been pregnant. Pay close attention to signs of student discomfort when discussing these concepts.

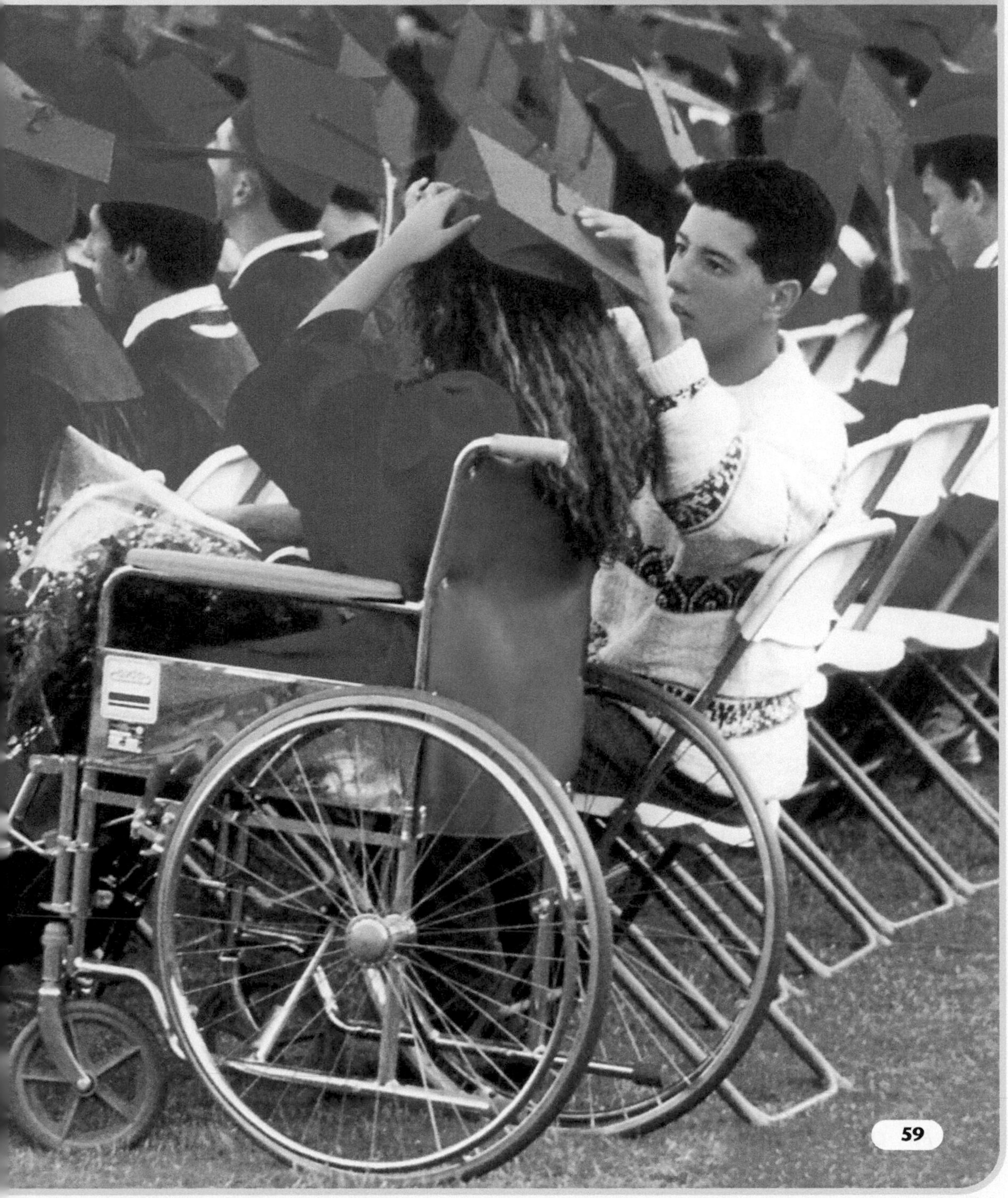

VIDEO 19

TEENS Talk

Teen Pregnancy

Video Objectives

Use the video to help students

Describe the extra challenges that teen parents face.

Explain why prenatal care is especially important for teen mothers.

Evaluate the sacrifices and setbacks to life goals experienced by teen parents.

Preview **Activity**

How Would Your Plans Change?

Assign the Preview Activity in class before showing the video. After students complete the activity, ask for volunteers to share their conclusions about how parenthood would affect both their weekend plans and their long-term plans. Summarize the themes that emerge from the discussion.

From the Authors

Any discussion about pregnancy can cause a normally responsive class to sink into an embarrassed silence. Not only can pregnancy and birth be scary, it also involves the female reproductive system. For discussions about pregnancy and prenatal care, shift the focus to a hypothetical married couple.

Students may also be uncomfortable with discussions of contraception. Again, it might be helpful to discuss this situation in the context of a hypothetical married couple. Make it known that inappropriate laughter and crude comments about any of these topics will not be tolerated.

ABILITY LEVELS

- **L1** For students with special needs
- **L2** For less proficient readers
- **L3** For all students
- **L4** For gifted and talented students
- **EL** For English language learners

Section 1

Marriage and Family Decisions

Objectives
Before class begins, write the objectives on the board. Have students copy the objectives into their notebooks at the start of class.

1. Focus

***Warm-Up* Health Stats**

After students have completed their writing, ask several volunteers to share their responses with the class. Students' responses may include the increase in the number of young people pursuing higher education or the increase in the number of women working outside the home.

Connect to Your Life *Sample answer:* I think that friendship is the most important part of a successful marriage.

Section 1

Marriage and Family Decisions

Objectives

- **List** three keys to a successful marriage.
- **Identify** the lifelong responsibilities of parenthood.

Vocabulary

- **compatibility**
- **commitment**
- **compromise**

Warm-Up

Health Stats What trend does this graph show?

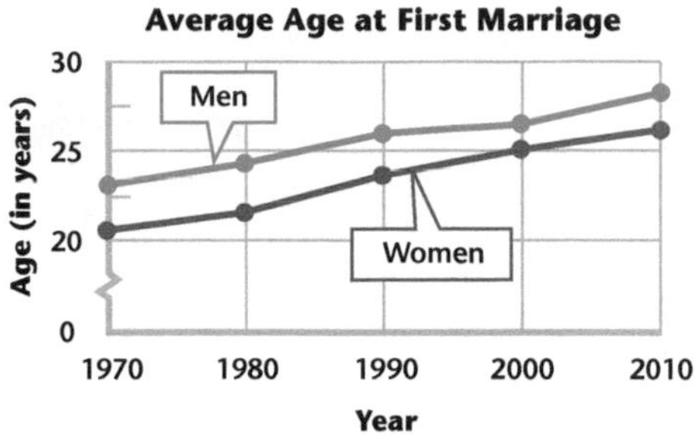

WRITING Describe some factors that may have contributed to this trend.

Marriage

During adolescence, many teens start to think about what it would be like to be in a committed, long-term relationship such as marriage. Some teens look forward to making such a commitment. Others are reluctant. Some feel that they may never be ready to take such a step.

More than 70 percent of all Americans marry at some time during their lives. Therefore, it is likely that you will marry someday. If you do choose to marry, it will probably be one of the most important decisions you will make. It will affect you, your spouse, your family, your friends, and possibly future generations. Understanding the challenges of marriage can help you to know when you are ready to take such a step.

Connect to Your Life **What do you think is the most important part of a successful marriage?**

WRITING and Health

L3 Communication in Marriage

Ask students to describe in their private journals two examples of communication in marriage that they have observed. They should describe at least one example of good communication and one of bad communication. They should also explain why they categorized each example the way that they did. WRITING

FIGURE 1 Successful marriages require the couple to make many adjustments, such as becoming members of different families.

Why People Marry People marry for a variety of reasons. Some people marry because they desire another person's love and companionship. Others marry for financial, social, or cultural reasons.

You need to know yourself fairly well before you select a marriage partner. You need to know what your goals are and how you are going to achieve them. You need to know what is important to you. When it comes time to marry, people usually select marriage partners who have similar interests, values, level of education, and social background to themselves. People who are quite different from each other can also have successful marriages, but they may have to work harder to overcome their differences.

Successful Marriages You probably feel, as most people do, that successful marriages are based on love. But what is love? Often young people mistake sexual attraction or short-lived crushes for love. Real love is part of a long-lasting relationship in which people really know, like, and accept each other. People who are truly in love appreciate the things they like about each other and accept the things they dislike. When you love someone, his or her well-being becomes as important to you as your own.

Although love is a basic element in a successful marriage, it is not the only one. **Love, compatibility, and commitment are key factors in a successful marriage. Compatibility** is the ability to live together in harmony. **Commitment** is the strong determination by the couple to make their marriage a fulfilling lifelong relationship.

There are several other important factors that contribute to most successful marriages.

- **Ability to Compromise** Even the most compatible couples will disagree occasionally. During a **compromise,** each partner gives up something to reach an agreement.
- **Communication** Partners should be able to share their thoughts and feelings. Each should trust the other to listen and accept what is being said without making judgments.
- **Sexual Intimacy** Sexual intimacy in marriage is an expression of mutual physical attraction, emotional intimacy, and love.

2. Teach

Marriage

L3 Cultural Connection

Many cultures have customs related to weddings and marriages. Ask students to describe any of these customs with which they are familiar. Then ask students to identify common elements of marriage and wedding customs from the different cultures.

L2 Class Discussion

Ask students to examine the list of qualities that make a marriage successful. Ask students to discuss reasons why each of these factors is important to a marriage. Ask: **Why is the ability to compromise an important part of a successful marriage?** *(Sample answer: In a marriage, you cannot always get your own way. Compromise is necessary to resolve conflicts as they arise.)* Ask students to brainstorm other qualities to add to the list.

L4 Active Learning

Have students prepare a ten-question survey on how responsibilities in a marriage are shared. Have each student ask five husbands and five wives to respond to the survey. Ask students to compile the class results and create graphics or visuals to summarize the results. MATH

Differentiated Instruction

EL English Language Learners

Ask students to work with a partner to review the qualities that contribute to a successful marriage. Ask students to identify any unfamiliar terms. Then, have students work with their partner to use a standard dictionary to find the meanings of these terms. Have students use index cards to record the definitions of the terms. Ask students to work with their partner to practice pronouncing these terms and using them in spoken sentences.

L3 Building Health Skills

Communicating Explain that stresses and conflicts are a part of all marriages. Marriages are successful when partners are able to use good communication skills to manage their differences. Divide the class into small groups. Assign each group a potential source of marital conflict related to division of household chores (for example, who is going to do the dishes?). Have the members of each group write a dialogue showing how this conflict could be resolved in a positive way by using good communication skills. Ask each group to share its dialogue with the class.

L2 Visual Learning: Figure 2

Have students examine the graph that shows the relationship between a woman's age at marriage and the probability of divorce. Ask: **How do divorce rates for women who marry as teens compare to divorce rates for women who marry after age 25?** *(The divorce rate for women who marry as teens is consistently higher than that of women who marry after age 25.)*
Caption Answer 30 percent of those who marry under age 18 divorce in the first five years of marriage.

L3 Journal Writing

Have each student write a journal entry that lists goals that he or she hopes to achieve between the ages of 17 and 25. In their journal entry, have students write a few sentences that summarize how teen marriage could impact these goals. Remind students that they will not be required to share their journal entries. **WRITING**

Stresses in Marriage Throughout marriage, a couple must be willing to make adjustments to meet each other's needs. The changes in attitudes and expectations that these adjustments require can produce stress.

One difficult adjustment in marriage can be determining the responsibilities that each spouse will have. Some couples decide early in their marriage how each person will contribute financially and who will do certain household tasks. By compromising and accepting tasks that fit their abilities and schedules, a couple usually can develop a comfortable give-and-take relationship. When changes occur, such as the birth of a child, the couple may need to redefine their responsibilities.

Marriages can become strained when unexpected problems arise. One spouse may lose his or her job. A family member may become seriously ill. Effective communication can help a couple get through a crisis. Sometimes a couple may need to seek financial or counseling services. Turning to family or friends for emotional support is another way to get through hard times.

Teen Marriage When teenagers marry, they often face additional challenges compared with those who marry later. The strains of adjusting to a new relationship, earning a living, and completing an education can feel overwhelming. Many married teenagers drop out of school. Without a high-school diploma, it can be difficult to find a good job. The couple may end up living with relatives. Such an arrangement can limit a couple's opportunities to make decisions and to develop as a couple.

Another difficulty for married teenagers involves changes in their friendships. Unmarried friends may not have the same interests and goals as a married couple, especially if the couple has a baby. A married couple may be concerned about stretching a small income, while single friends may be more concerned about school or dating.

It is difficult to know when you are 17 or 18 just who you will be when you are 25 or 30. People change a great deal during their teens and early twenties. For this reason, most teenagers choose to wait before making a long-term commitment. They want to find out more about themselves and to have other experiences first.

FIGURE 2 Divorce rates are typically higher for couples who marry in their teens.
Reading Graphs What percentage of marriages in which the wife is under age 18 when she marries end in divorce within the first five years?

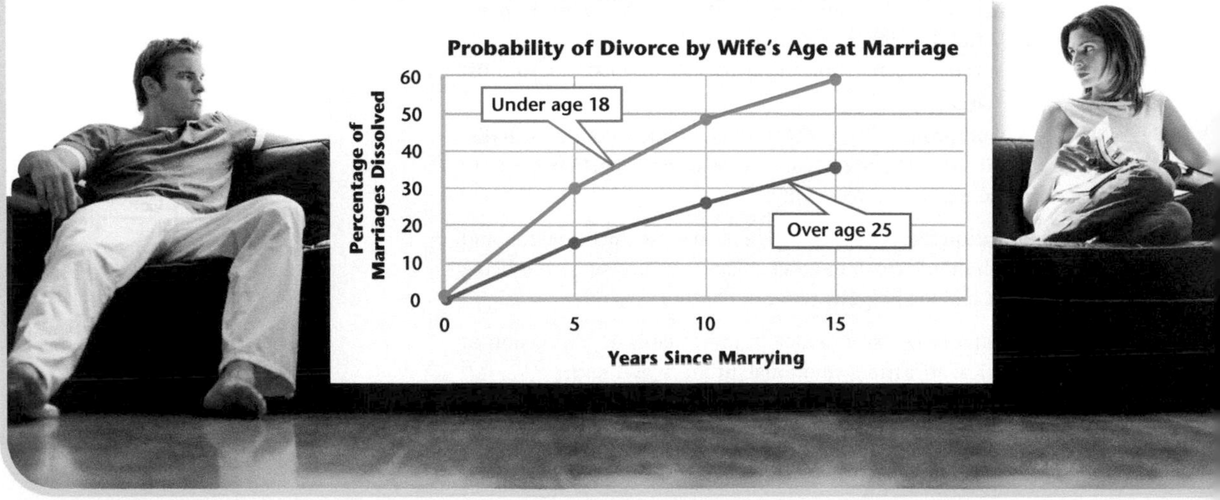

MATH and Health
L3 Percentages

According to the United States Department of Agriculture, a two-parent family with an annual income at or below $41,700 will spend an average of $134,370 to raise one child to the age of 17. (This figure does not include any college costs.) The cost is broken down as follows:
Housing: $44,480
Food: $26,490
Transportation: $18,660
Clothing: $8,490
Health Care: $10,680
Child Care/Education: $12,090
Miscellaneous: $13,380
Have students determine the percentage of the total cost that is represented by each of these categories and make a pie graph that displays the information. *(Answers rounded to the nearest whole number: Housing 33%, Food 20%, Transportation 14%, Clothing 6%, Health Care 8%, Child Care/Education 9%, and Miscellaneous 10%)*

Parenthood

For some people, adulthood is not only a time for marriage, but also a time to become parents. Parenthood has many joys and satisfactions, but it is also stressful and involves a lot of hard work. Along with the loving feelings, smiles, and cuddles, new parents face sleepless nights, worries about illnesses, and the loss of many freedoms they used to enjoy.

The responsibilities of parenthood go far beyond those of most occupations. **Parents need to be able to commit a lifetime of love, guidance, and attention to their children.** The relationship between parent and child is critical to the child's healthy development.

At least one part of making the decision to become parents is purely practical. A couple should review their budget to find out whether they can afford to provide food, clothing, and medical care for a child. They need to discuss who will care for the child if both spouses continue to work. They need to find out if their employers grant maternity or paternity leave, so that at least one of them can stay home with the baby for a few months and still return to the same job. They may also need to investigate the costs and availability of child care.

FIGURE 3 Before becoming parents, a couple should make sure they are ready to carry out the responsibilities of parenthood to the best of their ability.

Section 1 Review

Key Ideas and Vocabulary

1. What are three keys to a successful marriage?
2. Explain how **compatibility** contributes to a successful marriage.
3. What does **commitment** mean in the context of marriage?
4. Describe the lifelong responsibilities of parenthood.

Critical Thinking

5. **Relating Cause and Effect** What advice would you give to a friend who thinks that having a baby will help her relationship grow stronger?

Health and Community

An Interview With Adults Interview three adults—a young adult, a middle-aged adult, and an older adult. Ask them what advice they would offer to teenagers who are trying to set goals for the future. Compare the responses of the people you interviewed. What did you learn about planning for the future? WRITING

6. **Applying Concepts** Ryan and Linda have been arguing over how to spend some extra money. Ryan wants to buy a new car. Linda wants to buy new furniture. Suggest a way for Linda and Ryan to compromise.

Parenthood

L2 Active Learning

Have students interview their parents about how their lives changed when they became parents. Ask students to write down what they perceive as three positive changes and three negative changes that come with parenthood. Have volunteers share their responses with the class. WRITING

3. Assess

Evaluate

These assignments can help you assess students' mastery of the section content.

L3 Section 1 Review

Answers appear below.

L2 Reteach

Ask students to review the boldface headings and the figures in the section. Then have students make a concept map showing the different aspects of marriage and parenthood.

L4 Enrich

Health and Community

An Interview With Adults *Sample answer:* The responses to my interview questions indicate that adults in all three age groups would encourage teens to continue with their education as part of achieving their goals. I also learned that planning for the future is valuable, but I must be able to adapt to unexpected changes in my plans.

Section 1 Review

1. love, compatibility, commitment
2. Compatibility is the ability to live together in harmony, which is important for a successful marriage.
3. Commitment is the strong determination by the couple to make their marriage a fulfilling, lifelong relationship.
4. Lifelong responsibilities of parenthood include love, guidance, and attention.
5. *Sample answer:* I would tell her that having a baby is not the way to make a weak relationship stronger. A relationship must be strong to withstand the stresses of parenthood.
6. *Sample answer:* Ryan could agree to buy a used car instead of a new car so that there is money left over. Linda could agree to buy only one item of furniture for now and wait to buy the rest.

Section 2

Development Before Birth

Objectives
Before class begins, write the objectives on the board. Have students copy the objectives into their notebooks at the start of class.

1. Focus

Warm-Up Quick Quiz

After students finish writing, ask them to share the factors they thought married couples should consider before having children. List their responses on the board. Discuss the problems with reasons 1, 3, and 4. Also discuss whether 2 and 5 are good enough reasons on their own, or if prospective parents should consider other factors as well.

Sensitive Issues

Discussing the process of conception may be awkward for you and your students. As a strategy to minimize the awkwardness without skipping this important topic, briefly review with students how and where fertilization occurs, then shift the lesson's focus to the development of the fertilized egg.

Section 2

Development Before Birth

Objectives

- ▶ **Summarize** the events that occur during the first week after fertilization.
- ▶ **Describe** the structures that protect and nourish the embryo and fetus.

Vocabulary

- zygote
- embryo
- blastocyst
- implantation
- amniotic sac
- placenta
- umbilical cord
- fetus

Warm-Up

Quick Quiz Which of the following statements made by a married couple do you think are good reasons for having a baby? Choose one or more.

1. "It's now or never. We're almost 40."
2. "We have lots of love to give a child."
3. "If we have one more, maybe it will be a girl."
4. "Our marriage will improve if we have a baby."
5. "With our new jobs, we've finally saved enough money to start a family."

WRITING In a paragraph, describe the factors you think a married couple should consider before they have children.

▼ **Sperm surrounding an egg**

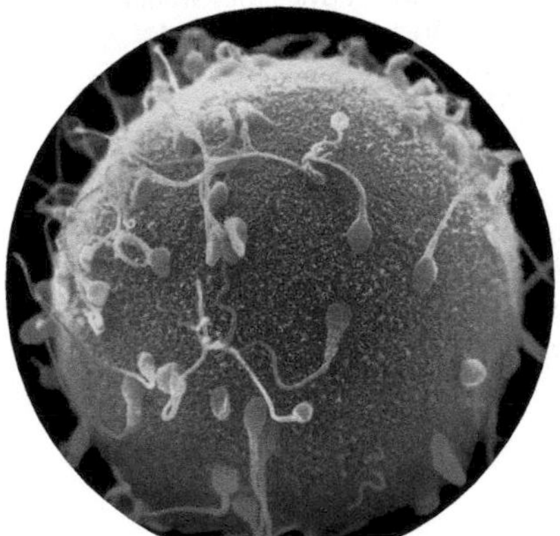

The Beginning of the Life Cycle

The birth of a baby is an incredible event. For parents, the nine months or so that precede their child's birth are filled with expectations. The years afterward are times of both hard work and wonder.

As a teenager, you may be curious about the physical processes of pregnancy. You may also think about the responsibilities and challenges that you may face one day as a parent. Understanding how human life begins and what pregnancy involves will help you to make responsible decisions now and in the future.

When a couple decides to start a family, they may try to conceive, or get pregnant. Recall from Chapter 2 that, in a fertile woman's body, about once a month an egg enters one of the fallopian tubes and begins its journey to the uterus. During sexual intercourse, sperm from the man are deposited into the vagina. Some of these sperm swim through the uterus to the fallopian tubes. If an egg is present in a fallopian tube, a sperm may fertilize it. This moment of fertilization is also called conception.

WRITING and Health

L3 Firsthand Account

Have students write a fictional firsthand account that describes the growing embryo's journey from the fallopian tube to the uterus. Students should include all the events that occur as the embryo makes this journey, beginning with the formation of the embryo after the zygote divides and ending with the implantation of the blastocyst. Suggest that students use Figure 4 to guide them through their story. Remind students that because this is a firsthand account, they should describe this journey from the perspective of the growing embryo.

1 Fertilization In Figure 4, you can track the events that occur in the first week after fertilization. Of the hundreds of millions of sperm that enter the vagina during sexual intercourse, only a few hundred usually make it to the egg, and only one can fertilize it. Within seconds of fertilization, the surface of the egg changes so that no more sperm can enter the egg. **In the first week after fertilization, the fertilized egg undergoes many cell divisions and travels to the uterus.**

2 The Zygote The united egg and sperm is called a **zygote** (ZY goht). Within 36 hours, while the zygote is still traveling through the fallopian tube, it begins to divide.

3 Cell Division The original cell divides to make two cells. From the two-cell stage until about nine weeks after fertilization, the growing structure is called an **embryo** (EM bree oh). As the embryo travels toward the uterus, its cells continue to divide.

4 The Blastocyst About five days after fertilization, the embryo reaches the uterus, where it floats for a few days. By this time, it is made up of about 50 to 100 cells. The structure, called a **blastocyst** (BLAS tuh sist), is no longer a solid mass of cells, but a sphere of cells with a hollow center.

5 Implantation Once the blastocyst forms, it begins to attach itself to the wall of the uterus. The process of attachment is called **implantation.**

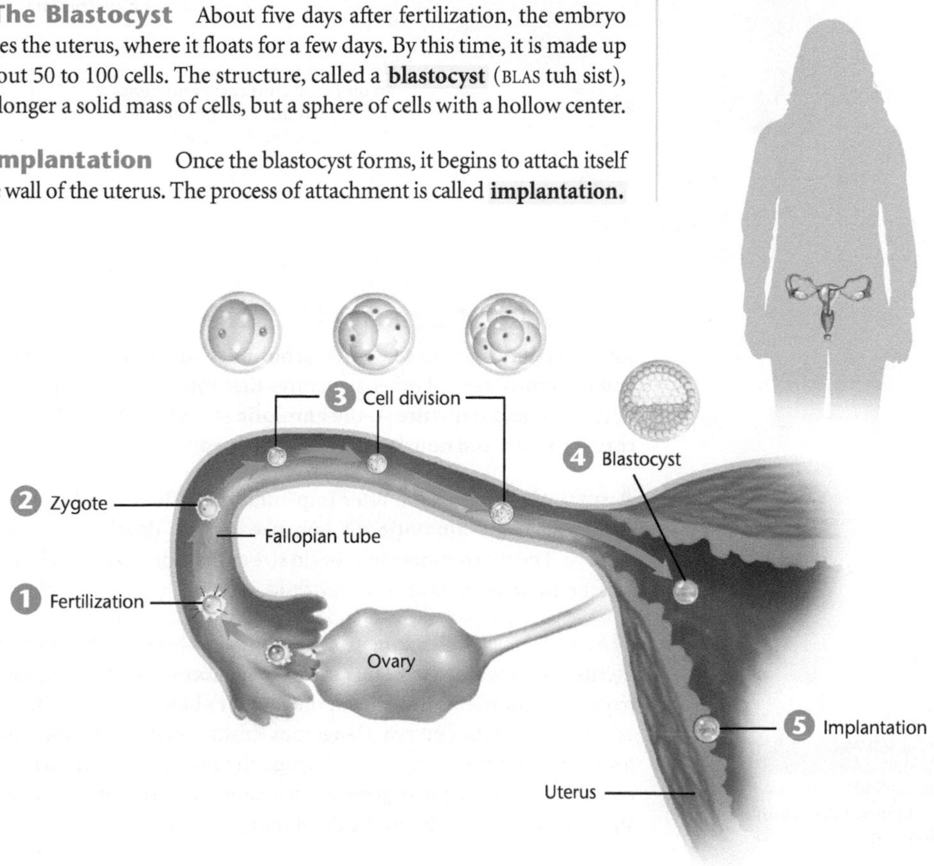

FIGURE 4 The fertilized egg travels to the uterus in the first week of pregnancy.
Interpreting Diagrams Through which structure does the embryo travel before reaching the uterus?

2. Teach

The Beginning of the Life Cycle

L3 Active Learning

Have students construct a time line on poster board that shows the stages and time frame of the development of an embryo during the first week. Students should begin the time line with fertilization and end it with implantation. They should also describe the location of the developing embryo through time. The time line should include these terms: zygote, cell division, embryo, blastocyst, and implantation.

L2 Visual Learning: Figure 4

Use Figure 4 to discuss the development of a fertilized egg. Begin with fertilization, pointing out that it occurs in a fallopian tube and that only one sperm fertilizes the egg. Then ask: **What is the fertilized egg called?** *(zygote)* **How long does it remain a zygote?** *(until it divides into two cells)* **About how long does it take the embryo to travel to the uterus?** *(about five days)* Point out the structure of the blastocyst. Explain that the outer group of cells will develop into a membrane that will nourish and protect the embryo. The inner group of cells forms the embryo.
Caption Answer fallopian tube

Differentiated Instruction

EL English Language Learners

Identify vocabulary terms for students to learn based on their level of understanding. For beginning English language learners, use the terms *embryo, placenta,* and *fetus.* Add *umbilical cord, implantation,* and *amniotic sac* to the list for intermediate students. Have students make flashcards for each term they are given. Students should include definitions, phonetic spellings if needed, and illustrations to help them with meaning.

Development in the Uterus

L2 Visual Learning: Figure 5

Image Bank Figure 19-2

Ask students to name the supportive structures associated with the embryo. *(amniotic sac, placenta, umbilical cord)* Then ask: **What is the amniotic sac?** *(a fluid-filled bag of thin tissue around the embryo)* **How are the functions of the placenta and the umbilical cord similar?** *(Both carry nutrients and wastes between the mother and embryo.)*

L3 Teacher Demo

Demonstrate how amniotic fluid acts as a shock absorber. Attach a string with strong glue to each of two small balls. Suspend each ball in a separate jar or clear plastic container by tying the end of the string to a pencil that lies across the top of the container. Fill one container with water so the ball is underwater. (Use balls that do not float, such as golf balls.) Then jiggle both containers with the same amount of force. Have students compare the movement of the balls. *(The ball in water will not swing as quickly as the ball in air.)* Then have students explain how amniotic fluid can cushion the embryo from shock. *(The amniotic fluid absorbs the force of the motion.)*

L1 Active Learning

To help students conceptualize the size of the fetus at various stages, have them use rulers to measure and mark off on a piece of paper one inch (eight-week embryo), 11 inches (average length of six-month fetus), and 20 inches (average length of a newborn). Show students pictures of the developing embryo at each of these stages. Then encourage students to find items in the classroom that are similar in size.

Connect to Your Life Microscopic organisms in the fish could pass from the mother to the embryo and harm the embryo.

L3 Online Activity GO ONLINE

Visit Pearson SuccessNet to access an online activity about development before birth. Have students complete the Web activity.

FIGURE 5 The embryo is surrounded by several protective structures.

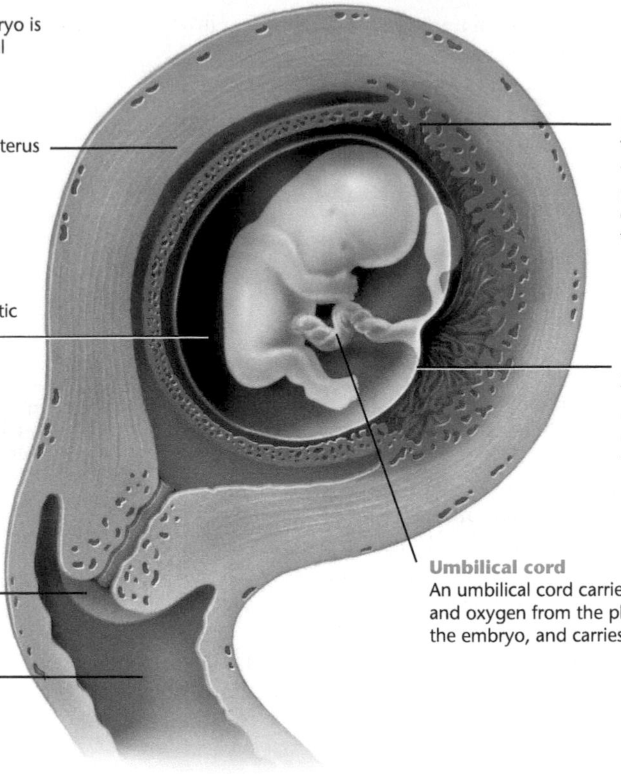

Development in the Uterus

After implantation, development continues in the uterus. While the embryo grows, several other structures that you can see in Figure 5 also develop. **These structures—the amniotic sac, placenta, and umbilical cord—protect and nourish the developing embryo, and later the fetus.**

Amniotic Sac Soon after implantation, a fluid-filled bag of thin tissue called the **amniotic sac** (am nee AHT ik) develops around the embryo. The sac continues to grow in size as the embryo grows. Inside the sac, the embryo floats in amniotic fluid.

Placenta The attachment holding the embryo to the wall of the uterus develops into a structure called the **placenta.** Within the placenta, oxygen and nutrients move from the mother's blood into tiny blood vessels that lead to the embryo. Dangerous substances can pass from mother to embryo, too, including alcohol, drugs, the chemicals in tobacco smoke, and some microscopic organisms that cause disease. Any of these substances can seriously harm the developing embryo.

GO ONLINE
PearsonSuccessNet.com
For: More on development before birth

Connect to Your Life **Why do you think pregnant women are cautioned to avoid eating raw fish?**

TEENS *Are Asking . . .*

Q: Since a fetus doesn't breathe, how could the mother's smoking habit cause harm?

A: Smoking increases the carbon monoxide levels in the mother's blood. Blood that contains carbon monoxide cannot carry normal amounts of oxygen, so the amount of oxygen available to the embryo or fetus is reduced. In addition, the nicotine in cigarette smoke causes blood vessels to get narrower, reducing the amount of blood that can enter the placenta. With less blood entering the placenta, less oxygen and fewer nutrients are available to the fetus.

Together, these effects of smoking during pregnancy slow fetal growth, which may cause the newborn to be underweight and at greater risk for health problems.

Umbilical Cord About 25 days after fertilization, a ropelike structure called the **umbilical cord** (um BIL ih kul) develops between the embryo and the placenta. The umbilical cord is the embryo's lifeline. Blood vessels in the umbilical cord carry nutrients and oxygen from the placenta to the embryo and wastes from the embryo to the placenta.

The Growing Embryo During the first two months of development, the major body systems and organs start to form in the embryo. For example, a basic heart, major blood vessels, kidneys, and endocrine glands develop. By the end of eight weeks, the embryo is about an inch long and has recognizable external features such as eyes, ears, arms, and legs. The head is large in proportion to the body—it makes up nearly 50 percent of the length of the embryo.

The Fetus From the start of the third month until birth, the developing human is called a **fetus.** During the third to sixth month, the fetus begins to move and kick, a sign that its skeleton and muscles are developing. As its nervous system matures, the sense organs begin to function. The fetus becomes sensitive to light and sound and alternates periods of activity with periods of sleep.

From the seventh to the ninth month, the fetus continues to grow and develop. The size of the body increases so that it is more in proportion to the size of the head, and body fat accumulates. The eyelids open and close. By the end of the ninth month, the fetus is ready to be born.

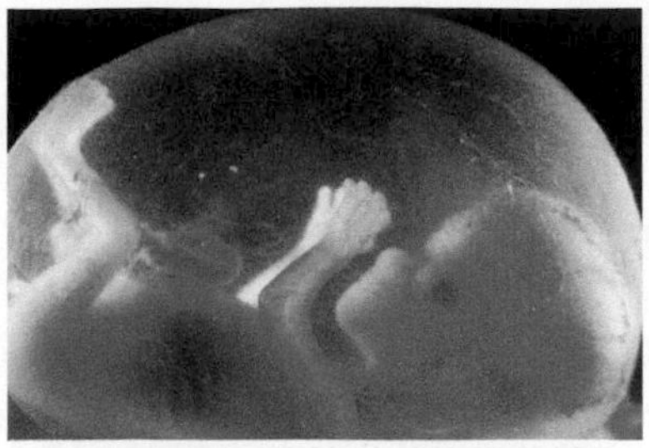

▲ **Fetus at 3 months**

▼ **Fetus at 8 months**

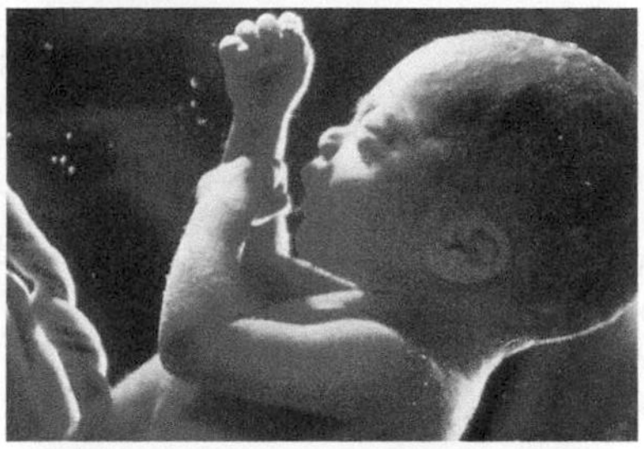

FIGURE 6 Between the third and eighth month of development, the facial features and limbs of a fetus change dramatically.

Section 2 Review

Key Ideas and Vocabulary

1. What happens during the first week of human development?
2. What happens during **implantation**?
3. What three structures protect and nourish the embryo, and later the fetus?
4. What is the **placenta**? What is its function?
5. How does a **fetus** change between the third and sixth months of pregnancy?

Critical Thinking

6. **Calculating** Suppose that only 200 sperm out of the original 400 million sperm deposited in the vagina survive the journey to the egg. What percentage is this? MATH
7. **Relating Cause and Effect** Why is it an unhealthy decision for a pregnant woman to drink alcohol?
8. **Sequencing** List in order the following steps of development: eyelids open and close, legs kick, embryo is about an inch long, amniotic sac develops.

Health and Community

Support for New Parents Many communities offer free support groups for new parents. At the support group, parents can share the joys and frustrations of caring for their newborn. They may also learn new skills, such as how to bathe, diaper, and give first aid to their baby. Find out what services your community offers and make a pamphlet for new parents. WRITING

3. Assess

Evaluate

These assignments can help you assess students' mastery of the section content.

L3 Section 2 Review

Answers appear below.

L2 Reteach

Have students describe to a partner the events that occur from the time an egg is fertilized to the time the fetus is ready to be born. Students can use the information in Figures 4, 5, and 6 to help them describe these events.

L4 Enrich

Health and Community

Support for New Parents Many hospitals provide these types of support groups for new parents. Suggest that students contact local hospitals, medical clinics, or public health agencies for more information. Tell students that pamphlets should include information about these services, their costs, and whom to contact to get more information.

Section 2 Review

1. The fertilized egg undergoes many cell divisions and travels to the uterus.
2. The embryo, in the form of a blastocyst, attaches to the wall of the uterus.
3. the amniotic sac, placenta, and umbilical cord
4. a structure that lines part of the wall of the uterus; nourishes the embryo with substances from the mother's blood
5. The fetus begins to move and kick, its sense organs begin to function, and it alternates periods of activity with sleep.
6. $200 \div 400{,}000{,}000 = 0.0000005 \times 100 = 0.00005\%$
7. The chemicals in alcohol can pass to the embryo and harm it seriously.
8. amniotic sac develops, embryo is about an inch long, legs kick, eyelids open and close

Section 3

Pregnancy

Objectives
Before class begins, write the objectives on the board. Have students copy the objectives into their notebooks at the start of class.

1. Focus

Warm-Up Myth/Fact

Ask students to share their do's and don'ts for pregnant women. List them on the board. Refer back to this list throughout the section, correcting any misconceptions that students might have had.

Section 3

Pregnancy

Objectives

- **Identify** four behaviors that are essential for a healthy pregnancy.
- **Explain** the importance of prenatal care throughout pregnancy.
- **Describe** the risks associated with teen pregnancy.

Vocabulary

- **prenatal care**
- **obstetrician**
- **trimester**
- **ultrasound**
- **chorionic villus sampling**
- **amniocentesis**
- **ectopic pregnancy**
- **miscarriage**
- **preeclampsia**
- **gestational diabetes**

Warm-Up

Myth A pregnant woman doesn't need to visit the doctor until she begins to show, or look pregnant.

Fact Regular doctor visits from the beginning of pregnancy until the birth of the baby are recommended to ensure health.

WRITING List some other do's and don'ts for pregnant women. Review and update your list when you complete this section.

Staying Healthy During Pregnancy

Amanda starts her day with a bowl of oatmeal. Later, she and her husband go out for a brisk walk. At night, she skips a party where people will be smoking.

Amanda and her husband are thinking about having a baby. Even before she becomes pregnant, Amanda has started taking extra care to have a healthy pregnancy. **Getting proper nutrition and exercise and avoiding drugs and environmental hazards are especially important both before and throughout pregnancy.**

Proper Nutrition "Now you're eating for two," people sometimes say to pregnant women. This is because a pregnant woman needs to eat more calories to support the growth of her own body and the developing embryo or fetus. During pregnancy, a woman needs to consume about 300 extra calories a day. The best way to obtain these extra calories is to eat a well-balanced diet rich in the key nutrients listed in Figure 7.

One vitamin that is especially important during pregnancy is folic acid, or folate. Folic acid is essential for proper development of an embryo's neural tube, which later develops into the spinal cord and brain. The neural tube forms early in an embryo's development, often before a woman knows she is pregnant. Therefore, a woman should not wait until she knows she is pregnant to get enough folic acid. Doctors recommend that all women of childbearing age consume at least 0.4 mg (400 micrograms) of folic acid every day.

For Your INFORMATION!

Changes During Pregnancy

Almost every organ and system in a woman's body is affected by pregnancy. The most important changes occur in the reproductive system. Ovulation and menstruation cease. The muscular walls of the uterus get stronger and more elastic. The cervix produces a mucus plug that prevents bacteria from entering the uterus.

A pregnant woman also experiences physiological changes that allow sufficient blood and oxygen to reach the growing embryo. Her heart beats slightly faster, and the volume of blood circulating in her body increases. The amount of oxygen her body uses increases by 15 to 20 percent.

Exercise Regular physical activity is also important for a healthy pregnancy. A fit woman will better meet the extra energy demands of carrying the fetus. She also reduces her risk for diabetes and other health problems during pregnancy. A woman should get her doctor's approval for her exercise program. Some forms of exercise should be avoided—for example, horseback riding, where there is a high risk of falling.

Avoiding Alcohol and Other Drugs As soon as she plans to become pregnant, a woman should abstain from all alcohol, tobacco, and any other drugs not prescribed or approved by her doctor. These substances, even in small amounts, can harm or kill the developing baby, decrease the newborn's chance to live, or cause lifelong problems.

For example, women who drink alcohol during pregnancy risk having a baby with fetal alcohol syndrome. Symptoms of fetal alcohol syndrome may include mental retardation, minor to severe heart defects, and delayed growth. Drug use during pregnancy can also lead to a baby having low birthweight, or weighing less than 5.5 pounds at birth. These babies face an increased risk of health problems as newborns and throughout life.

Some drugs that are typically safe outside of pregnancy can cause harm to a fetus. A pregnant woman should talk to her doctor before using any prescription drugs or over-the-counter drugs, including pain medications, creams and lotions, and vitamins. Likewise, a woman should get her doctor's approval before drinking herbal teas or using other herbs.

Connect to Your Life **Which recommendations for pregnant women are also good everyday advice for yourself?**

FIGURE 7 Proper nutrition contributes to the healthy development of a baby. **Reading Tables** Name three nutrients that play a role in the development of the nervous system.

Important Nutrients During Pregnancy

Nutrient	Needed For
Folic acid	Formation of neural tube; brain and spinal cord development
Protein	Muscle formation and growth
Calcium	Bone and tooth formation; nerve and muscle development
Iron	Oxygen delivery by blood cells
Vitamin A	Cell and bone growth; eye development
Vitamin B complex	Nervous system development

2. Teach

Staying Healthy During Pregnancy

L3 Active Learning

Explain that pregnant women can participate in many forms of exercise, but are also cautioned from participating in some. Suggest students speak to physical education teachers at school, physical fitness instructors at a local gym, or an obstetrician to find out which forms of exercise are not appropriate for pregnant women and which forms are highly recommended. Have students prepare an informational brochure targeted to pregnant women that summarizes their findings. **WRITING**

L2 Visual Learning: Figure 7

Review the nutrients listed in Figure 7. Discuss food sources of these vitamins and minerals. Explain that pregnant women are routinely given vitamin supplements as part of their prenatal care. Ask: **Why should women who are considering pregnancy get adequate amounts of these nutrients?** *(Critical embryonic development has already occurred before a woman realizes that she is pregnant.)*

Caption Answer folic acid, calcium, vitamin B complex

Connect to Your Life *Sample answer:* proper nutrition, exercise, and avoiding alcohol and other drugs

Differentiated Instruction

L2 Less Proficient Readers

After students read about the four behaviors that are essential for a healthy pregnancy, have them create a word web that summarizes the reading. Suggest that students use the title of the subsection, Staying Healthy During Pregnancy, in the center circle of the web. Students can use the run-in headings to name the behaviors that branch from the center circle. Finally, students should add details in circles that are attached to each behavior.

L3 Building Health Skills

Advocacy Have students write an e-mail to an imaginary older cousin or sister who is newly pregnant. In their e-mails, students should describe one environmental hazard their cousin or sister might inadvertently come into contact with. Students should explain how this substance or organism can harm the growing embryo and advocate for avoiding it. **WRITING**

Prenatal Care

L2 Building Vocabulary

Point out the meanings of the Latin roots of the word *trimester*. *Tri-* means "three;" *mensis* means "month." Ask students to list and define other words beginning with the prefix *tri-*. (triangle, *a figure with three angles;* trilogy, *a story with three parts;* triplets, *three babies born at the same time to the same mother*) Then ask students to think of words that use the Latin root word *mensis.* (semester, *originally a school term of six months;* menstruation, *bleeding that occurs each month in fertile women)*

L3 Cooperative Learning

Explain to students that during visits to her doctor, a pregnant woman has an opportunity to ask questions about her pregnancy, as well as how to care for her baby after birth. Have student groups produce a list of questions that a woman might ask her doctor during a prenatal visit. Then ask groups to share their questions with the class.

Avoiding Environmental Hazards Some common substances found in the environment, including many chemicals and disease-causing organisms, can seriously harm a fetus. Pregnant women should take care to avoid exposure to these substances.

- **X-rays** The radiation from X-rays can harm a developing embryo or fetus. This is why doctors and dentists ask women if they could possibly be pregnant before taking an X-ray.
- **Lead** The main source of exposure to lead is from lead-based paint present in older homes. If a pregnant woman lives in a home built before 1978, she should contact her state health department for information on getting her home tested for lead.
- **Mercury** Most exposure to this dangerous metal comes from eating contaminated fish. Pregnant women should eat commercially caught fish only once a week, and should not eat swordfish or shark.
- **Cat Litter** Cat feces can contain a parasite that is especially dangerous to a developing fetus. Pregnant women should avoid contacting soiled cat litter or garden soil.

Prenatal Care

A woman also needs to plan for **prenatal care,** or medical care during her pregnancy. Her doctor visits should be under the supervision of an **obstetrician,** a doctor who specializes in pregnancy and childbirth. **The chances of having a healthy baby greatly increase if the mother visits her doctor or clinic for regular checkups throughout pregnancy.**

The Three Trimesters A pregnancy is divided into three periods of time—**trimesters**—each of which is approximately three months long. Figure 8 lists things the parents-to-be can expect at routine visits.

FIGURE 8 A doctor monitors the health of the mother-to-be and her fetus during regular prenatal visits.

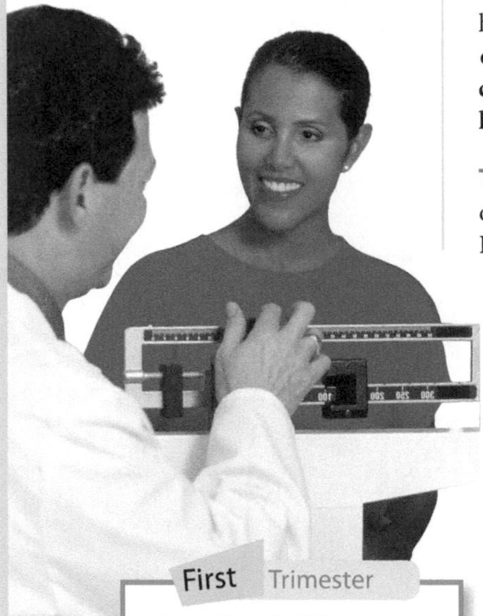

First Trimester
- Record medical history and weight
- Note conditions that could affect the pregnancy
- Prescribe prenatal vitamins as needed

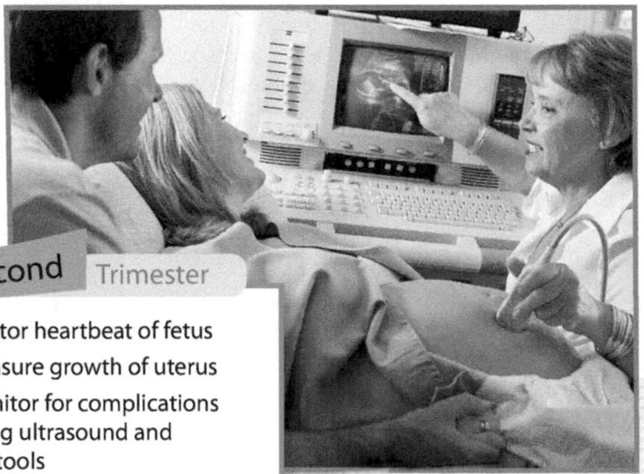

Second Trimester
- Monitor heartbeat of fetus
- Measure growth of uterus
- Monitor for complications using ultrasound and other tools

WRITING and Health

L2 Summary

Have students write a summary about how to stay healthy during pregnancy. Students should base their summaries on the four behaviors that are essential for a healthy pregnancy described in the section. Summaries should clearly differentiate between behaviors that should be practiced and behaviors that should be avoided. Challenge students to limit their summaries to one or two paragraphs.

Monitoring Tools Prenatal care gives a pregnant woman access to the latest medical tests and technologies.

- **Ultrasound** Did you know that your first pictures may have been taken months before you were born? High-frequency sound waves, or **ultrasound,** are used in most pregnancies to create an image of the developing fetus. Ultrasound may be used at any point during pregnancy, although it is typically used in the sixteenth to twentieth week. Using ultrasound, a doctor can tell the age of the fetus, whether it is a boy or girl, and if the heart, muscles, and bones are developing normally. Ultrasound may also detect the presence of more than one fetus or confirm the position of the fetus in the uterus.
- **Chorionic Villus Sampling** Around the eighth week of pregnancy, some women will undergo a test called **chorionic villus sampling,** or CVS. To perform the test, the doctor removes and tests a small piece of the developing placenta. CVS can detect inherited disorders in the embryo such as hemophilia or extra chromosomes. The test is only done when risk factors are present, such as a family history of genetic disorders or when the mother is over the age of 35. An older mother has an increased risk of having a baby with Down syndrome or other chromosomal abnormalities.
- **Amniocentesis** Another test that may be done around the fourteenth to sixteenth week of pregnancy is **amniocentesis** (am nee oh sen TEE sis). The procedure involves inserting a needle into the woman's abdomen and uterus to remove a small amount of amniotic fluid surrounding the fetus. The doctor then tests fetal cells naturally found in this fluid for abnormalities. Like CVS, amniocentesis is only performed when the fetus is at higher risk for a genetic disorder. CVS and amniocentesis are not routine tests because they slightly increase the risk of miscarriage, or death of the fetus.

Connect to Your Life **Have you ever seen an ultrasound picture of a fetus? What features could you recognize?**

Third Trimester

- Check position and size of fetus
- Check for warning signs of premature, or early, birth
- Continue to monitor for complications
- Discuss birth process

Differentiated Instruction

EL English Language Learners

The terms that describe the monitoring tools used during pregnancy and the possible complications of pregnancy might be difficult for students to say and comprehend. Work with students to create a notebook or bulletin board display of these terms. Include pictures or diagrams for terms that lend themselves to visuals (such as ultrasound and amniocentesis). Also include phonetic spellings and simple definitions. Have students practice saying the terms by pairing them with students who can pronounce the terms correctly.

L2 Visual Learning: Figure 8

Use the charts in Figure 8 showing typical events during prenatal checkups to begin a discussion on the importance of prenatal care. Ask: **What kinds of issues are addressed by the doctor during the first trimester?** *(preparing for future changes during the pregnancy, helping the mother change her behaviors to ensure a healthy baby)* **What is the focus of prenatal care during the second trimester?** *(the health of the mother and the developing fetus and possible complications)* **The third trimester?** *(getting ready for delivery and monitoring the fetus and mother for any health issues)* Explain that fathers are encouraged to accompany the mother during prenatal visits to give support, share in the joy of monitoring the growth of the fetus, and help make decisions about complications that might arise.

L1 Active Learning

Share pictures of ultrasound images of your own children or those of fellow teachers, friends, or family. Pass around the photos, or alternatively, make them into slides to project, and have students name any structures they can identify. Point out that internal structures, such as the brain, heart, stomach, and skeleton, are also imaged by ultrasound and may be visible in your pictures. Help students locate any internal parts that show up in your pictures. Remind students that ultrasound is a very useful, low-risk tool for doctors to check on the health of a fetus.

L3 Building Health Skills

Making Decisions Explain that it is possible for parents to learn the sex of their baby during pregnancy. Discuss the advantages and disadvantages of learning this information. Then ask students to write a paragraph explaining whether or not they would want to know the baby's sex if they had to make this decision. **WRITING**

Connect to Your Life Recognizable features include arms, legs, head, eyes, fingers, and toes.

L3 Content Update GO ONLINE

Visit Pearson SuccessNet to access more information about pregnancy care. Have students complete the Web activity.

L3 Cooperative Learning

Divide the class into groups of four or five, and assign each group one of the following pregnancy complications: ectopic pregnancy, preeclampsia, and gestational diabetes. For each complication, ask students to learn more about what it is and its possible causes, if known. Then challenge students to think of ways in which the complication might be prevented. Instruct students to make a poster that displays this information about the complication and present it to the class.

L2 Visual Learning: Figure 9

Invite students to compare the size of the baby in the photograph with the size of the adult's hand. Then ask: **Why do you think the hospital costs for premature babies are so much higher than the costs for healthy newborns?** *(Sample answer: Premature babies are in the hospital for a longer period of time and require more specialized care.)* Explain that in some cases, premature babies continue growing and developing in incubators where they receive only intravenous feedings until their digestive system is able to digest breast milk or formula.

GO ONLINE
PearsonSuccessNet.com
For: More on pregnancy care

Complications Problems can occur anytime during pregnancy. For some of these complications, timely treatment can reduce negative consequences or even save the life of the woman or fetus.

- **Ectopic Pregnancy** In the very rare case of an **ectopic pregnancy,** the blastocyst implants in the fallopian tube or elsewhere in the abdomen, instead of in the uterus. The embryo cannot develop normally and may put the mother's life at risk. Surgery is necessary to remove the embryo and repair the damaged fallopian tube.
- **Miscarriage** The death of an embryo or fetus in the first 20 weeks of pregnancy is called a **miscarriage.** Over 20 percent of pregnancies end in miscarriage. Miscarriage almost always occurs during the first trimester, sometimes before a woman knows she is pregnant. Miscarriage is usually caused by a serious genetic defect, but is sometimes due to illness or a drug the mother has taken. In other cases, there is no apparent reason for a miscarriage.
- **Preeclampsia** Also called toxemia, **preeclampsia** (pree ih KLAMP see uh) is characterized by high blood pressure, swelling of the wrists and ankles, and high levels of protein in the urine. Its onset is usually in the second or third trimester. Preeclampsia prevents the fetus from getting enough oxygen. This serious condition is treated with bed rest or medication.
- **Gestational Diabetes** Diabetes that develops in pregnant women is called **gestational diabetes,** and is marked by high blood sugar levels. Like preeclampsia, it usually develops later in pregnancy. If left untreated, excess blood sugar that passes through the placenta to the fetus may cause the fetus to grow too big. This increases the risk of a difficult birth, as well as breathing problems and obesity in the newborn.
- **Premature Birth** Delivery of a live baby before the 37th week of pregnancy is called premature birth. The earlier the birth, the more problems the baby tends to have. The lungs of a premature baby are usually not fully developed, and in some cases, the baby cannot breathe without help. A premature baby may receive care in an incubator, a chamber designed to protect the baby while he or she develops more.

FIGURE 9 A premature baby may need extended hospital care while his or her lungs and other organs continue to develop.

On average, hospital costs for premature babies are 14 times as high as costs for healthy newborns.

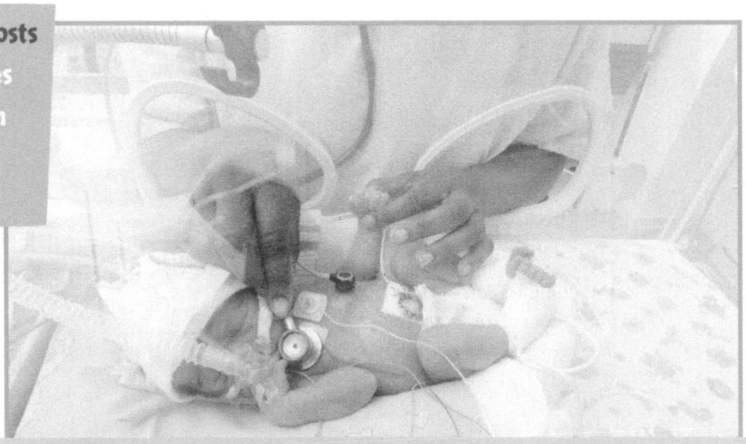

Differentiated Instruction

L4 Gifted and Talented

Have students research complications that can occur at birth and how these complications are handled. (Complications that students might choose include fetal aspiration of meconium during birth, unproductive labor, breech fetus, or an umbilical cord that is expelled before the fetus is delivered.) Students should prepare a presentation to the class on their findings using a poster, presentation software, or other visuals.

Teen Pregnancy

Each year in the United States, about 750,000 girls between the ages of 15 and 19 become pregnant. Almost another 20,000 girls under the age of 15 become pregnant. The vast majority of teenage pregnancies are unwanted. Why, then, is the number so high?

Some teens who choose not to be abstinent lack accurate information about birth control. Some teens believe myths rather than facts about birth control or do not follow directions carefully. Still others do not use birth control because they think, "it can't happen to me." By risking an unplanned pregnancy, teens place their futures in jeopardy.

Facing a Pregnancy A teen who finds that she is pregnant faces some tough decisions. She needs to consider her feelings, values, and circumstances, as well as those of the father and others close to her. Talking things over with a parent or another close relative, friends, a member of the clergy, or a counselor may help her understand her thoughts and concerns.

Babies born to teen mothers are at increased risk for low birthweight.

FIGURE 10 Because teens are still maturing physically, a teen's body may not be ready to support a developing baby. Babies born to teen mothers are at risk for many health problems.

Health Risks An unplanned pregnancy is an overwhelming experience at any age, but it is even more so for teenagers. **Pregnant teens face risks to their health and to the health of the fetus that most pregnant women in their 20s and 30s do not face.** For example, young teens are more likely to experience preeclampsia and premature birth.

There are many reasons why teens are more likely to experience complications during pregnancy.

- Teens are still growing and maturing. A teen's body may not be ready to support a developing baby.
- Many pregnant teens do not follow diets that provide adequate nutrition for both the baby and their own growing bodies.
- Pregnant teens are less likely than adult women to seek early prenatal care.

Babies of teenage mothers are also more likely to suffer health problems include low birthweight, birth defects, and delayed development. Getting adequate prenatal care throughout the pregnancy increases a teen's chance of having a healthy child.

Connect to Your Life **How would you give emotional support to a friend who became pregnant?**

Teen Pregnancy

L3 Active Learning

Arrange to have a teen mother, teen father, or teen parents come to class. Before the visit, have small groups brainstorm questions about how the parents' lives have changed and the challenges they have faced as parents. Review the groups' questions before the interview to make sure they are appropriate.

L4 Building Health Skills

Accessing Information Have students research and estimate approximately how much it would cost to support a child for one month. Assume the child is 2 years old and stays in a day-care center from 8 A.M. to 5 P.M., Monday through Friday. The child needs food, diapers, and a new pair of shoes during the month. Instruct students to make an itemized list of expenses and compute the cost. **MATH**

L2 Class Discussion

Ask students to come up with reasons why teens are less likely to get early prenatal care than adult pregnant women. Some possible responses are teens might not realize they are pregnant as early as adult women; a teen may be in denial about the pregnancy; it could take a long time for a teen to get the courage to tell a parent. Then ask students to explain how they would try to convince a pregnant friend to get early prenatal care.

Connect to Your Life Allow students to answer this question in their private journals.

TEENS *Are Asking . . .*

Q: A friend of mine says she would really like to have a baby now. Why would she want to have a baby when she is so young?

A: The idea of having a baby can seem appealing to teens who want to feel needed. They may think of a baby as a cute, cuddly companion who will always love them. Sometimes a teen might think that a baby would be a cure for loneliness or insecurity. But, the reality is quite different. Babies are totally dependent on someone to fulfill their every need. There is no break, even when the mother is sick or wants to do things with friends. Most teens who express a desire to have a baby are not considering the whole picture.

Hands-On *Activity*

Be a Parent for a Day

Suggest that students keep a written log or diary in which they record their thoughts and feelings as they take care of their "baby." Also have students record any lapses they had, how they chose a book to read to the "baby," and who took care of the "baby" if they had to go out.

Think and Discuss

1. *Sample answers:* My free time was limited; I found myself worrying about the baby; or I resented not being able to do what I wanted.
2. It is about the same size and weight as a baby.
3. The best time is when a couple is emotionally and financially ready to have a baby and has planned for the baby.

L3 Journal Writing

Have each student write a personal journal entry describing how life would be different if he or she had a baby. Ask students to consider how a baby would affect their free time, their friendships, their family relationships, and their goals for the future. If some students at first think that having a baby would be fun, writing about the realities of raising a baby as a teen parent can help them realize how difficult it would be. **WRITING**

Hands-On *Activity*

Be a Parent for a Day

Materials

5-pound bag of flour
plastic bag with tie

Try This

1. Place the bag of flour inside the plastic bag and fasten it shut. For the next 24 hours, you will be responsible for your bag of flour as if it were a real baby.
2. Choose a name for your "baby."
3. Follow these rules for taking care of your "baby."
   - Every 5 hours, including at night, feed your "baby" for 20 minutes. During this time, you must remain seated in one place and devote your full attention to your "baby."
   - Every 3 hours during the time that you are awake, allow 5 minutes for changing your "baby's" diaper.
   - Spend 15 minutes in the evening talking or reading to your "baby."
   - Never leave your "baby" alone. If necessary, arrange for someone to babysit.

Think and Discuss

1. How did being a parent of a bag of flour affect your lifestyle?
2. In what ways is a bag of flour an appropriate object to use
to represent a baby?
3. When do you think is the best time for a person to become a parent? Explain.

Being a Teen Parent Teenagers who decide to raise their children need to think about the help they will receive from other people in their lives. Some teen fathers want to be an important part of their child's life. Often, however, teen fathers are not any more prepared to take on parenthood than are teen mothers. If teen parents do stay together or marry, they often must leave school and have difficulty finding a decent job and an affordable place to live.

Many teen parents turn to their own parents for help. Some families are willing to take on some of this responsibility. However, not all families are able or willing to help. As a result, many teen parents find that they must figure out how to live on their own.

For anyone, being a parent can be stressful. For teens, this is especially true because they often lack the skills and experience needed to be good parents. Some communities have parent-training programs that teach parenting skills. These programs also provide a place for young parents to seek support when problems arise.

For Your INFORMATION!

Open vs. Closed Adoptions

In recent years, there has been an increase in the number of "open" adoptions in the United States. Because of differences among state laws, there is no simple definition for "open adoption." In general, an open adoption occurs when the adoptive parents know identifying details about the birthmother. In some cases, they may have even met. Proponents claim that this openness is better for all parties. Benefits include continued contact between the child and birthmother, the adoptive parents' ability to access the child's family health history, and reduced anxiety on the part of the birthmother about the child.

More traditional adoptions are usually referred to as "closed." In closed adoptions, the birthmother and adoptive parents do not know each other, and the birthmother has no contact with the child. Proponents of closed adoptions claim that its benefits include a sense of closure for the birthmother and less confusion for the child.

Adoption Some pregnant teens decide that adoption is the best choice for themselves and their babies. Adoption is a process by which a child becomes the legal responsibility of a parent or parents who are not the child's biological parents. An adoption should be handled by a public agency or a licensed private agency. This will help ensure that a child is adopted into a loving and financially secure home.

Deciding to give up a baby is difficult. It is normal for parents to wonder about the child for a long time after the adoption. Sharing these feelings with a counselor or other trusted individual can help a person cope with this difficult decision.

Ending a Pregnancy One of the options available to a pregnant teen who feels she cannot go through with the pregnancy is to end the pregnancy through abortion. Abortion is the medical termination of a pregnancy. The procedure is safest when it is performed within the first twelve weeks of pregnancy.

When deciding about whether to have an abortion, a woman of any age should seek counseling and accurate information. A teen may also need permission from a parent, legal guardian, or judge before the abortion can proceed.

Abortion is a highly controversial issue. Some people think that abortion is wrong and should be illegal. Others think that abortion should be legal, but be more restricted. Still others think that abortion is a personal decision that should remain legal.

Section 3 Review

Key Ideas and Vocabulary

1. List four healthy habits that a pregnant woman should adopt before and during pregnancy.
2. Why is prenatal care so important throughout pregnancy?
3. About how long is each **trimester** of a pregnancy?
4. What is **chorionic villus sampling**? Under what conditions is it sometimes recommended?
5. Describe three symptoms of **preeclampsia**. How is it treated?
6. Explain why a pregnant teen faces more health risks during pregnancy than a mature woman.

Health at Home

Ultrasound Pictures Ask your mother or other relative with children if she saved any ultrasound pictures from her pregnancy. Ask permission to see the pictures. Ask about her emotions during the ultrasound—was she scared, happy, excited? Write a paragraph about the pictures and the mother's experience. **WRITING**

Critical Thinking

7. **Evaluating** From the following list, which food choices are not generally recommended for pregnant women: swordfish, spinach, wine, herbal tea, dairy products?
8. **Comparing and Contrasting** How are chorionic villus sampling and amniocentesis alike? How are they different?

3. Assess

Evaluate

These assignments can help you assess students' mastery of the section content.

L3 Section 3 Review

Answers appear below.

L2 Reteach

Have students work in groups to create a poster that describes the four behaviors that are essential to a healthy pregnancy. Students should also add prenatal doctor visits and their importance.

L4 Enrich

Health at Home

Ultrasound Pictures Students' paragraphs should describe their impressions of the ultrasound pictures and the parts of the fetus they were able to discern. Students should also describe how the mother was feeling and how the ultrasound pictures affected those feelings.

Section 3 Review

1. get proper nutrition, exercise, avoid alcohol and other drugs, avoid environmental hazards
2. Prenatal care greatly increases the chances of having a healthy baby.
3. three months
4. A small piece of the placenta is removed and tested; when there is a family history of a genetic disorder or when the mother is over the age of 35.
5. high blood pressure, swelling of the wrists and ankles, high levels of protein in the urine; bed rest or medication
6. A teen's body may not be ready to support a developing baby. Pregnant teens are less likely to get adequate nutrition or seek early prenatal care.
7. swordfish, herbal tea, and wine
8. Similarity: Both tests are performed when the fetus is at risk for a genetic disorder. Difference: Fetal cells in the amniotic fluid are tested in amniocentesis. A piece of the placenta is tested in CVS.

Preventing Pregnancy

Objectives
Before class begins, write the objectives on the board. Have students copy the objectives into their notebooks at the start of class.

1. Focus

Warm-Up **Advice Line**

After students have completed their writing, ask several volunteers to share their responses with the class. Students' responses should include reliable sources of information such as healthcare professionals or medical resource books.

2. Teach

Abstinence

L3 Building Media Literacy
Ask students to compare how attitudes toward sexual intimacy among teens are portrayed in television programs. Have students work as a class to create a graphic organizer or chart that displays the answers to the following questions: "Is sexual activity between teens a part of this program?" "Is abstinence mentioned?" "Are the risks of sexual activity, such as pregnancy, discussed?" Follow up with a class discussion on realistic and unrealistic television portrayals of teen sexual intimacy.

Connect to Your Life Some students may offer cultural reasons or mention maintaining a positive relationship with their parents.

Section 4

Preventing Pregnancy

Objectives

- ▶ **Explain** why abstinence is the only completely effective way to prevent pregnancy and STIs.
- ▶ **Explain** why contraception is a responsible decision for those who choose to be sexually active.
- ▶ **Identify** the three general types of contraception.

Vocabulary

- **contraception**
- **effectiveness**
- **failure rate**
- **spermicide**
- **sterilization**

Warm-Up

Dear Advice Line,

My friends seem to think they know a lot about birth control, but I really don't think I should trust their advice. Where can I go to find reliable information about birth control?

WRITING Write a response to this teen with advice about where to find reliable information about birth control.

Abstinence

The only way for a person to eliminate the risks of pregnancy and sexually transmitted infections is to practice abstinence. Many teens feel that abstinence is the best decision for them at this point in their lives. Teens choose abstinence for a number of reasons.

- ▶ They think that sexual intimacy should be reserved for a long-term committed relationship, such as marriage.
- ▶ They do not feel ready to take on the added responsibilities that come with a sexually intimate relationship.
- ▶ They want to keep their focus on achieving current goals such as athletics or getting into college.
- ▶ They want to be certain to avoid pregnancy and sexually transmitted infections.

Choosing sexual abstinence does not mean avoiding intimate relationships. Abstinent couples have the opportunity to get to know each other on a deep emotional level and to develop a relationship based on understanding, caring, and trust.

Connect to Your Life **What other good reasons are there for choosing abstinence?**

Sensitive Issues

- Some students might be uncomfortable with this topic, especially if they feel that the use of contraception is wrong. Be attuned to students' comfort levels as you discuss this topic, and take into consideration the values of your community.
- Before teaching this section, check your school district's policies on teaching about contraception.

Contraception

Contraception, or birth control, is the use of an appropriate method to intentionally prevent pregnancy. There is a wide array of different contraceptive methods. **Couples who choose to be sexually active, but do not wish to have a child, must decide on a method of contraception that is right for them.** Many factors should be considered when choosing a contraceptive method.

- ▶ Can the method be purchased over the counter or is a prescription required?
- ▶ How much planning and preparation is needed?
- ▶ Does the product have health risks or side effects?
- ▶ Does the method protect against STIs, including HIV? If so, which STIs does it protect against?
- ▶ How effective is the method at preventing pregnancy?

Effectiveness The **effectiveness** of a contraceptive method is the likelihood that using the method will prevent pregnancy. Often, the effectiveness of a contraceptive method is measured by its **failure rate,** the percentage of pregnancies that result in one year in a group of people who use that method. The lower the failure rate, the higher the effectiveness.

Many factors contribute to a method's effectiveness. Sometimes a failure occurs through no fault of the couple. More often, however, a failure occurs because the couple did not follow instructions or didn't use the method *every time* they had intercourse. Figure 17 on page 82 compares the failure rates for the methods discussed in this section.

Getting More Information People who are sexually active need accurate information and advice about contraception. If possible, the best way to get advice is to ask a parent or another trusted adult. Doctors, other healthcare professionals, and counselors at family planning clinics are also reliable sources of information.

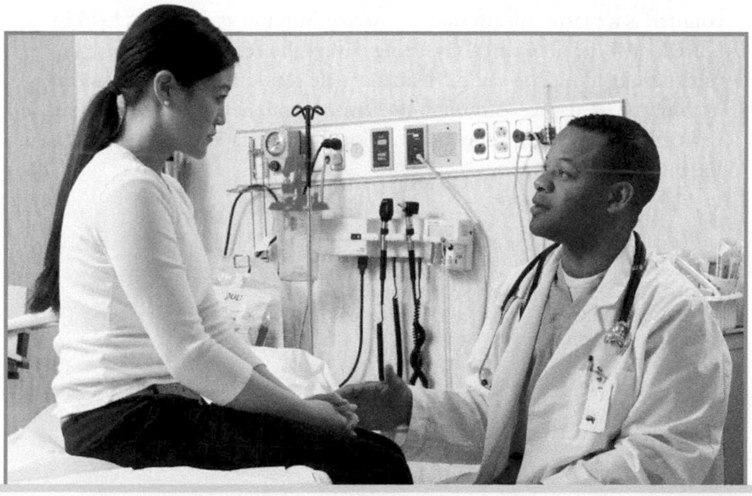

FIGURE 11 When seeking information about birth control, it is important to talk with an informed person who can be trusted, such as your doctor.

2. Teach

Contraception

L3 Active Learning

Many teens may be reluctant to ask questions about contraception in the presence of their peers. However, it is important that their questions are answered so that their concerns and misconceptions are addressed. Keep an anonymous question box somewhere in the room in which students can drop slips of paper with their questions.

L3 Addressing Misconceptions

Perfect Use vs Typical Use Students should be aware that the effectiveness of contraceptive methods can be expressed in two ways—perfect use or typical use. Perfect use refers to the percentage of couples who experience an unintended pregnancy within one year despite following instructions without fault and using the method every time they had intercourse. This percentage is often considerably lower than the percentage associated with typical use.

Typical use refers to the percentage of unintended pregnancies for couples whose use is inconsistent or not always correct (i.e., human error). For example, the typical use effectiveness of the male condom is about 16%, while the perfect use effectiveness is as low as 2%. When evaluating a method's effectiveness, one should really consider the typical use effectiveness more strongly than perfect use because, over the span of a year, even careful couples may make mistakes.

Differentiated Instruction

L4 Gifted and Talented

Have small groups suppose that they are coordinators of a local teen center that is developing a new program. The goal of the program is to provide teens with social activities to participate in that will help them build self esteem and avoid sexual activity. Have the groups develop a proposal that includes the following information: the specific activities that will be offered, advertising methods, cost, and how they will measure the success of the program.

Barrier Methods

L2 Visual Learning: Figure 12

Have students come up with more bullets to add to the list in Figure 12. For example: *should only use them with latex-safe lubricants; should not reuse a condom; should use latex condoms for greatest protection against STIs; should never substitute a plastic bag or plastic food wrap for a condom.*

L3 Addressing Misconceptions

Ineffective Barriers Emphasize to students that nothing is a substitute for a condom. Plastic bags, plastic food wrap, or rubber balloons should never be fashioned into makeshift condoms. Those materials are not designed to protect against pregnancy or STIs.

L3 Building Health Skills

Communicating There are many excuses that someone may use to avoid using a condom during sexual activity. Emphasize that if someone—male or female—chooses to be sexually active, condoms are crucial for avoiding STIs and pregnancy. Ask students to come up with responses to some typical excuses for not using condoms. For instance: "But it doesn't feel as good with a condom." *(If you don't use a condom, then we need to stop.)*; "But I don't have any condoms with me." *(Then we better go get some.)*; "But I'm allergic to latex." *(Then we'll use one made of polyurethane.)*; "But I take birth control pills, so we don't need a condom." *(Birth control pills do not protect against STIs).*

FIGURE 12 Male condoms are an effective way of preventing pregnancy and STIs when they are used correctly.

Barrier Methods

Most contraceptive methods fall into one of three categories—barrier methods, hormonal methods, and permanent methods. Barrier methods prevent sperm from reaching an egg. Some methods, such as condoms, diaphragms, cervical caps, shields, and sponges, are physical barriers. Others, such as spermicide, are chemical barriers.

Male Condom One form of contraception that can be purchased over the counter is the male condom. The male condom is a thin sheath that fits over an erect penis. Condoms prevent pregnancy by stopping sperm from being released into the vagina.

Condoms are made of latex, polyurethane, or animal intestine. While all of these types can prevent pregnancy, latex condoms provide the best protection against STIs. Even latex condoms, however, do not provide protection from all types of STIs. See Chapter 5 for more information.

Some condoms contain a **spermicide,** a chemical agent that kills sperm. Because spermicide may increase the risk of HIV transmission, the Centers for Disease Control and Prevention (CDC) recommends the use of condoms *without* spermicide.

Condoms must be used carefully and consistently to prevent pregnancy and the transmission of STIs.

- Condoms must be rolled over an erect penis before any penetration of the vagina occurs.
- If the condom does not have a reservoir tip to collect semen, a small space—about one-half inch—should be left between the tip of the penis and the condom.
- The male should withdraw while the penis is still erect. As he withdraws, he should hold the rim of the condom at the base of the penis.
- A condom cannot be reused. It should be discarded immediately.
- Condoms should not be exposed to heat, lotions, or petroleum-based products, which weaken latex.

Female Condom The female condom, which is available over the counter, is a plastic sheath that is inserted into the vagina. It is held in place by two flexible rings. One ring covers the cervix. The other ring remains outside of the vagina. Like the male condom, a female condom can only be used once. Although the female condom does provide some protection from STIs, it does not provide the same level of protection as the male condom.

FIGURE 13 The female condom lines the inside of the vagina and forms a barrier that prevents sperm from entering the woman's body.

For Your INFORMATION!

Latex Allergy

A small percentage of people are allergic to latex. Males or females who have this allergy may experience burning, itching, or swelling in the penile or vaginal areas after using a latex condom. People with a latex allergy can use polyurethane condoms or animal skin condoms to prevent pregnancy. However, animal skin condoms do *not* provide adequate protection against STIs, including HIV.

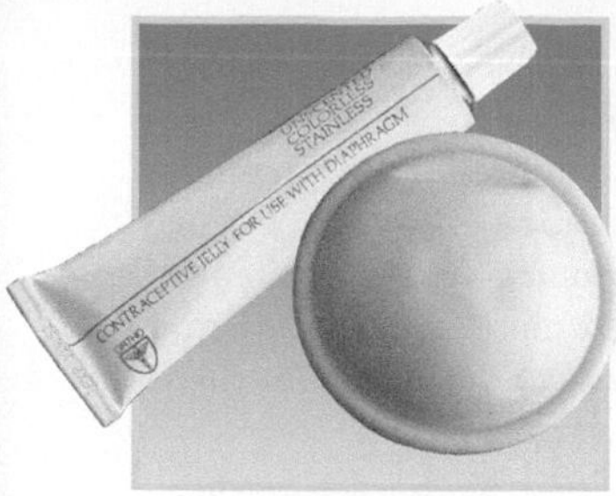

▲ **Diaphragm**

▲ **Cervical Cap**

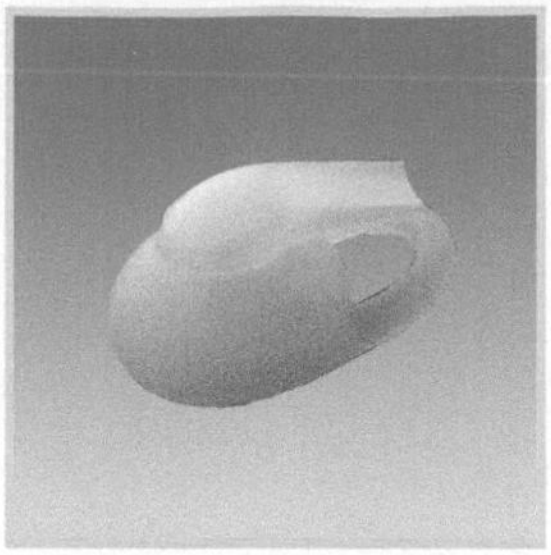

▲ **Shield**

FIGURE 14 These devices block sperm from reaching the cervix, while the spermicide applied to them acts to kill the sperm.

The Diaphragm, Cap, and Shield Three barrier contraceptive methods that are available only by prescription are the diaphragm, cervical cap, and shield. All three devices cover the cervix and block sperm from entering the uterus.

The diaphragm and cervical cap are dome-shaped cups made of soft rubber or latex. The cervical cap is smaller than the diaphragm. A female must see her healthcare professional to be measured for the proper-sized diaphragm or cervical cap. After a weight gain or weight loss of 10 pounds or more, or a pregnancy, she should be fitted again.

A shield, which is made of silicone, has a valve that helps keep the device in place. The shield comes in only one size.

The diaphragm, cap, and shield share some similarities.

- The devices do *not* protect against STIs.
- Spermicide must be applied to them before they are inserted.
- They must remain in place for the recommended amount of time (usually 6 to 8 hours) after intercourse to prevent pregnancy.
- To avoid infection, they should be removed within the instructed amount of time.
- They can be washed and stored for repeated use.

The Sponge The sponge is a disk-shaped, foam device that contains spermicide. Sponges can be purchased over the counter. Before intercourse, the sponge is moistened with water and then inserted into the vagina. After intercourse, the sponge should be left in place for at least six hours but not more than 30 hours. Sponges are thrown away after use. The sponge does *not* protect against STIs.

Spermicides Although spermicides can be used alone as a contraceptive method, it is recommended that they be used in conjunction with another more reliable method. Foams, jellies, and creams are three types of spermicide products. They are inserted into the vagina with an applicator. Insertion should occur no more than 30 minutes before intercourse.

A contraceptive suppository is a small capsule that contains spermicide. It must be inserted into the vagina 10 to 15 minutes before intercourse so that it has time to dissolve. Spermicides do *not* protect against STIs.

L2 Cooperative Learning

In small groups, have students create charts in which to compare the advantages and disadvantages of barrier methods of contraception. The chart should list all the barrier methods discussed in this chapter.

EL Building Vocabulary

Break down the word *spermicide* for students. Tell them that the suffix *–icide* comes from the Latin *caedere* which means "to kill." Point out that it contains the same word root as many other words in the English language, such as homicide and pesticide.

L3 Class Discussion

The diaphragm, cap, shield, and sponge all work in a similar way—they block sperm from crossing the cervix and entering the uterus. All four devices must be used with spermicide. Ask students to think of reasons why only the sponge can be purchased over the counter. (*The diaphragm and cap must be fitted; A healthcare provider should teach the woman the proper way to insert a prescription method; It's important that the woman understand how to care for the prescription methods because the devices are cleaned and reused.*)

For Your INFORMATION!

Intrauterine Devices (IUDs)

One barrier method that is not discussed in this section is the IUD. An IUD is a contraceptive device that is implanted in the uterus. The device emits either copper or hormones that interfere with the function of eggs and sperm. An IUD can be a very effective and convenient method of birth control for adult women. However, a teen's uterus may be too small to secure an IUD. Even some adult women cannot use an IUD until after they have had a baby.

Planning for the Future **79**

Hormonal Methods

L2 Cooperative Learning

Review with students the different schedules for each type of hormonal contraceptive method. For example, the pill must be taken every day, the patch must be changed once a week, and a new ring must be inserted every month. Divide the class into small groups, and have each group make a list of the advantages and disadvantages of each method's schedule. Lead a class discussion on how the effectiveness of each contraceptive method depends strongly on the individual using it consistently and correctly.

L3 Addressing Misconceptions

Students may have heard the term *emergency contraception.* Emergency contraception comes in two forms: hormone-containing pills or an intrauterine device (IUD). They work in one of three ways: by preventing ovulation, by keeping the sperm from meeting the egg, or by preventing implantation of a fertilized egg in the uterus. Emergency contraception is not the same thing as the so-called "abortion pill," which induces a miscarriage after an embryo has implanted in the uterus. Still, emergency contraception is controversial because some people consider it to be a form of abortion.

Be sure that students realize that emergency methods are not intended for use as regular birth control. Side effects from emergency contraceptive methods may include nausea, vomiting, and irregular bleeding.

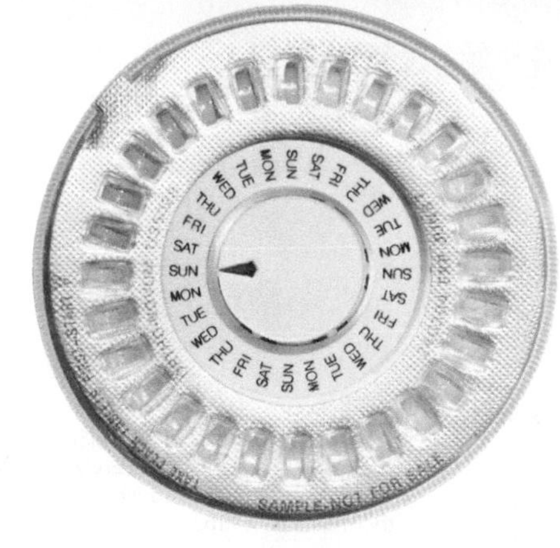

▲ **Oral contraceptives**

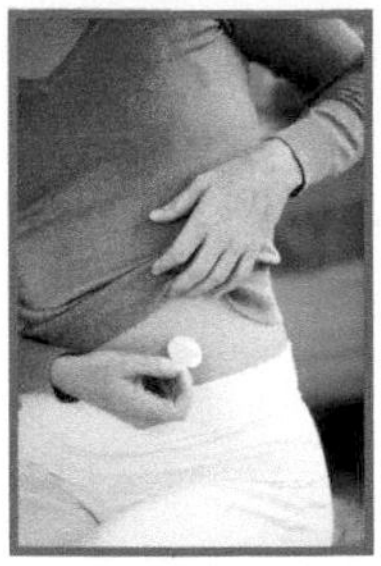

▲ **Skin patch**

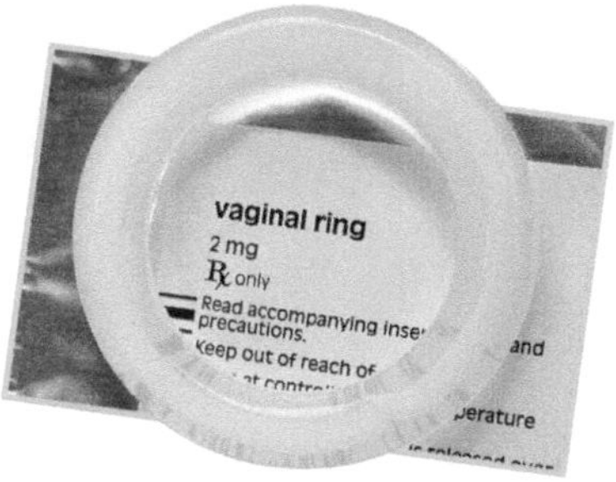

▲ **Vaginal ring**

FIGURE 15 Hormonal methods are highly effective, but cause more side effects than other methods. The side effects usually subside after a few months.

Hormonal Methods

Hormonal methods of contraception work by preventing ovulation or inhibiting fertilization. Currently, the only available hormonal methods are for females and require a prescription. All of these methods are more effective than barrier methods, but users are more likely to experience side effects. Hormonal methods do *not* protect against STIs.

Oral Contraceptives ("The Pill") Oral contraceptives usually come in packs of 28 pills. A female takes one pill each day, regardless of how often she has intercourse. If she forgets to take a hormone-containing pill for one or more days, a back-up contraceptive may have to be used for a period of time. Oral contraceptives come in two general forms.

- **Combination Pill** The combination pill contains synthetic versions of the female hormones estrogen and progestin (a hormone that is similar to progesterone). The hormones prevent ovulation—that is, they prevent the ovaries from releasing eggs. Side effects of estrogen-containing pills may include dizziness, nausea, and changes in menstruation. Rarely, users may experience cardiovascular problems such as high blood pressure and blood clots.
- **Mini Pill** The mini pill contains only progestin and may not prevent ovulation. Instead, it causes the mucus around the cervix to thicken. The thick mucus prevents sperm from reaching an egg. The mini pill is often prescribed to females who experience side effects from estrogen or who are breastfeeding.

Patches Another hormonal method is a skin patch, which is worn on the lower abdomen, buttocks, or upper body. The patch prevents ovulation by releasing estrogen and progestin through the skin. The patch is changed once a week. Patch users may have a higher risk of blood clots than combined pill users.

Rings The vaginal ring is a flexible ring containing hormones that a female inserts into her vagina. The walls of the vagina hold the ring in place. The ring is worn for three weeks and then removed while the female has her menstrual period. At the end of the fourth week, a new ring is inserted.

Injections A female may also receive an injection of progestin every three months. It is recommended that a female does not receive injections for more than two years in a row due to a risk of bone loss.

TEENS *Are Asking . . .*

Q: Will there be a male contraceptive pill?

A: There have been clinical studies on hormonal contraceptives for males. One type is in the form of a pill that a male must take every day, much like the female pill. The male pill contains a hormone that blocks sperm production. This effectively reduces a male's sperm count so that he cannot get a woman pregnant. Like the female pill, the male pill's effects are reversible, and it has not been shown to have any long-term effects on fertility. Some men have experienced side effects from the pill that are very similar to the side effects women experience from the female pill.

Other forms of hormonal contraceptives for males may include implants, injections, or patches. If and when a hormonal contraceptive for males is approved by the FDA, it remains to be seen if male hormonal contraceptives will become as widely used as female hormonal contraceptives.

Permanent Methods

Permanent methods of contraception are only appropriate for people who are sure that they either do not want any children or do not want more children. **Sterilization** is the use of surgery or other procedures to make a person incapable of reproduction. Sterilization does *not* protect against STIs. Because sterilization makes it no longer possible for a person to have children, it is a major life decision. Sometimes these procedures can be reversed with another surgery, but the chances are unlikely.

Vasectomy A male can be sterilized by a procedure called a vasectomy. A doctor makes a small incision in the scrotum and then severs each vas deferens, the tubes that carry sperm from the testes. The male still releases semen during ejaculation, but after four to six weeks the semen does not contain sperm.

Tubal Ligation The most common method of sterilization for females is called tubal ligation. During this procedure, a woman's fallopian tubes are cut or closed, blocking sperm's access to a released egg.

Sterilization Implant Another sterilization option for a female is to have a small, coiled implant inserted in each fallopian tube. Scar tissue forms around the implants, blocking the passageway of eggs and sperm. Unlike tubal ligation, this method does not require an incision. Neither method affects a woman's sexual function or menstrual cycle.

FIGURE 16 During sterilization, each vas deferens in males and each fallopian tube in females are altered. The sperm or eggs are no longer able to travel their normal path.

Vasectomy Each vas deferens is tied and cut.

Tubal Ligation Each fallopian tube is cut and sealed.

Sterilization Implant A coiled implant is inserted into each fallopian tube.

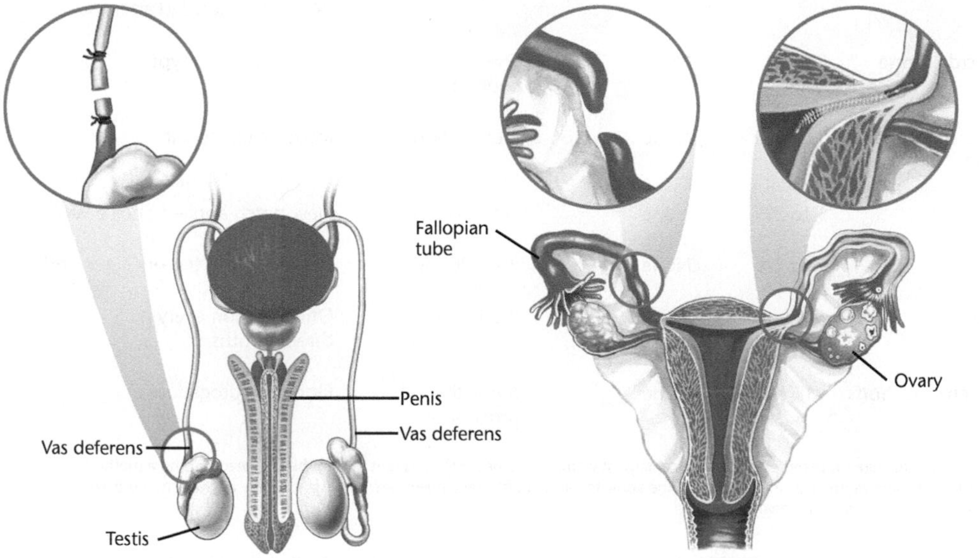

L3 Class Discussion

Tell students that the contraceptive pill is not prescribed solely for the prevention of pregnancy. Some adolescents may take birth control pills to regulate their menstrual cycles or to ease severely uncomfortable menstrual periods. Others may take birth control pills because they are taking another medication that would cause serious harm to a developing fetus. One type of acne medication, for example, can only be prescribed if a female is also using a reliable form of birth control.

Permanent Methods

L2 Visual Learning: Figure 16

Use Figure 16 to help students understand why permanent contraceptive methods are effective. Begin by discussing or reviewing the normal path of egg and sperm during development and fertilization. Then discuss how each permanent method interferes with the normal path, and thus prevents fertilization from occurring.

EL Building Vocabulary

Understanding the origin of the term *vasectomy* will help students decipher other similar medical terms. The suffix *–ectomy* comes from the Greek *tomos* which means "cut" or "slice." This suffix is used in many medical terms that refer to the removal of an organ such as *appendectomy* (removal of the appendix), *hysterectomy* (removal of the uterus), and *tonsilectomy* (removal of the tonsils). Explain that, in the case of a vasectomy, each vas deferens is severed rather than removed.

Differentiated Instruction

L2 Less Proficient Readers

Assign small groups two of the hormonal methods discussed in this chapter. Have the students create Venn diagrams in which to list the similarities and differences between their assigned methods. For example, a similarity of all the methods is that they do not protect against STIs. If you assigned one group the combination pill and the patch, a second similarity would be that they both prevent pregnancy by preventing ovulation. A difference would be that the pill is taken daily, while the patch is changed monthly. Have each group present their Venn diagram to the class.

L2 Class Discussion

Have students examine the failure rate column in Figure 17. Ask: **Which contraceptive methods have the highest failure rates?** (*spermicide alone, cervical cap, diaphragm)* **The lowest failure rates?** *(permanent methods, hormonal methods)* Then turn students' attention to the proper use column of the table. Ask: **How does the proper use of the methods with the highest failure rates differ from the proper use of methods with the lowest failure rates?** (*The methods with the highest failure rates have fairly complicated instructions for proper use compared to methods with lower failure rates.*) Have a volunteer summarize the connection between ease of use and failure rate. (*The easier the method is to use, the lower its failure rate.*) Ask students to consider the role that ease of use should play in choosing a contraceptive method.

FIGURE 17 When deciding on a contraceptive method, a person should carefully evaluate the effectiveness of each option.

Effectiveness of Contraceptive Methods

Contraceptive Method	Failure Rate*	Protection from STIs	Availability	Proper Use
Abstinence	0%	Complete		
Male condom	11%	Some	Over the counter	Applied immediately before intercourse; used once
Female condom	21%	Limited	Over the counter	Inserted before intercourse; used once
Diaphragm plus spermicide	17%	None	Prescription	Must be left in place for 6 hours after intercourse; can be washed and reused
Cervical cap plus spermicide	17 to 23%	None	Prescription	Proper insertion can be difficult; must be left in place for 8 hours; can be washed and reused
Shield plus spermicide	15%	None	Prescription	Must be left in place for 8 hours; can be washed and reused
Sponge	16%	None	Over the counter	Must be left in place for 6 hours; no additional spermicide required for 24 hours; discarded after use
Spermicide alone	35%	None	Over the counter	Varies based on type
Combined pill or Mini pill	1 to 2%	None	Prescription	Must be taken daily
Patch	1 to 2%	None	Prescription	New patch applied once a week
Ring	1 to 2%	None	Prescription	New ring inserted once a month
Injection	<1%	None	Prescription	One injection every three months
Permanent methods	<1%	None	Medical procedure	One-time procedure

* These approximate failure rate represents the percentage of women who become pregnant during the first year of using a method. The rates for the diaphragm, cap, shield, and sponge apply to women who have never been pregnant. These devices are more likely to fail in women who have been pregnant.

MATH and Health

L3 Graphing Failure Rates

Challenge students to create a graph showing the contraceptive failure rates listed in Figure 17. Students should decide which type of graph would be most appropriate for the data (bar graph). Students should draw their graphs on graph paper and include a title and *x*- and *y*-axis labels. If necessary, correct any errors. Then display students' graphs in the classroom. Ask: **Which representation of contraceptive failure rates makes it easier to compare failure rates—the table or the graph?** (*Most students will say the graph.*)

82 *Chapter 4*

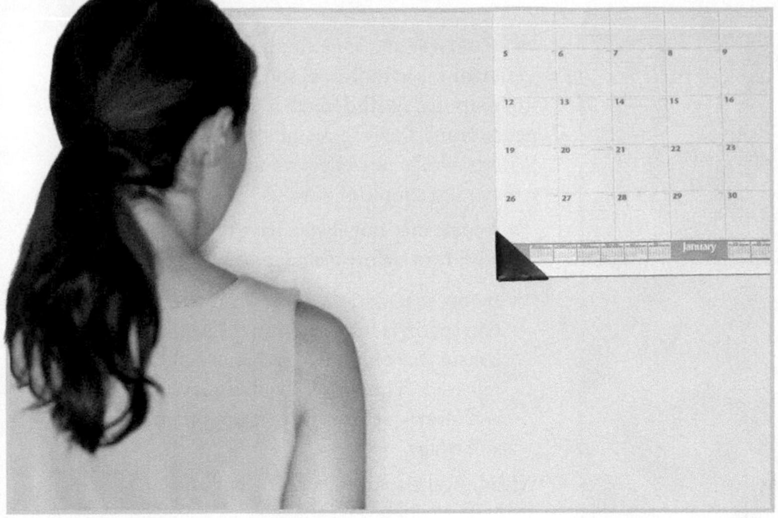

FIGURE 18 Periodic abstinence is a contraceptive method best used by adult couples who do not want to use barrier or hormonal birth control methods.
Comparing and Contrasting Why isn't periodic abstinence a reliable method of contraception for teens?

Unreliable Methods

To ensure the prevention of pregnancy, it is important that couples understand how and why the efffective methods of contraception work. Unfortunately, even when information about effective methods of birth control is available, some people use methods that do not work. **Knowing why unreliable methods are ineffective can help a person separate inaccurate information from accurate information.**

Periodic Abstinence Couples who practice periodic abstinence abstain from intercourse during the days of the female's cycle when she is likely to become pregnant. This method is also known as natural family planning or fertility awareness.

To practice periodic abstinence, a woman must pay careful attention to the days of her cycle. Some women also monitor symptoms such as body temperature, the color of cervical mucus, and breast tenderness to predict when they will ovulate. Several factors can decrease a woman's ability to make accurate predictions about her menstrual cycle.

- sickness or medications
- emotional stress
- alcohol or tobacco use
- change in sleep cycle

For careful and attentive women with predictable menstrual cycles, periodic abstinence can be as effective as barrier methods. However, periodic abstinence is *not* reliable for adolescents. It can take many years for a female's cycle to become regular enough for her to accurately predict when she will ovulate during each cycle. Also, periodic abstinence does *not* protect against STIs.

Unreliable Methods

Visual Learning: Figure 18

Caption Answer Periodic abstinence is an unreliable method for teens because a teen's menstrual cycle is usually not regular enough to allow accurate predictions of ovulation. Plus, periodic abstinence does not protect against STIs.

L3 Journal Writing

Ask students to think about with whom they would discuss contraceptive methods when they are ready to make such a decision. Have them record their response in their private journals. They should explain why they chose the person that they did. **WRITING**

L3 Class Discussion

Ask volunteers to share other examples of unreliable methods of contraception teens may have misconceptions about. You may be surprised by some of their answers. Either ask students to explain why the methods are unreliable or provide an explanation yourself. If the class seems reluctant to give examples aloud, have them write down the examples and submit them anonymously.

Differentiated Instruction

L2 Less Proficient Readers

Have students make a chart with three columns. In the first column they should list unreliable contraceptive methods. In the second column they should describe the methods. In the third column they should explain why the methods do not work. If you have a class discussion about other unreliable methods that are not discussed in the text, have students add those unreliable methods to their chart.

3. Assess

Evaluate

These assignments can help you assess students' mastery of the section content.

L3 Section 4 Review

Answers appear below.

L2 Reteach

Draw a scale of effectiveness on the board, with the far left indicating least effective and the far right indicating most effective. Ask students to tell you where each method of contraception should be placed on the scale.

L4 Enrich

Health at School

Comparing Contraceptives Student posters should include thorough and accurate information about the different methods of birth control. Display the posters in the classroom.

FIGURE 19 Couples who fail to make decisions together about reliable contraception may face an unplanned preganancy.

Withdrawal One method that is unreliable for anyone is withdrawal, sometimes called "coitus interruptus." Withdrawal is the removal of the penis from the vagina just before ejaculation. Withdrawal is not effective for preventing pregnancy for a couple of reasons.

- A male may not always have the self-control to withdraw before ejaculation.
- Before ejaculation, some fluid that may contain sperm is released from the penis. The male has no way of knowing when this fluid may be released. Therefore, even if he successfully withdraws before ejaculation, pregnancy can still occur.

Withdrawal also does *not* protect against STIs.

Other Unreliable Methods Females who use douching as a form of birth control hope that the douching will kill or wash the sperm out of the vagina. Sperm, however, can go through the cervix and enter the uterus just seconds after ejaculation. Douching, in fact, may help propel the sperm into the uterus.

Urinating after unprotected intercourse has no effect on preventing pregnancy. Because urine flows through the urethra and sperm are ejaculated into the vagina, urine does not wash away or kill sperm.

Section 4 Review

Key Ideas and Vocabulary

1. Explain why abstinence is the only 100 percent effective way to prevent pregnancy and STIs.
2. List five factors a couple should consider when choosing a contraceptive method.
3. What does the term **effectiveness** mean in reference to a contraceptive method?
4. Describe how barrier, hormonal, and permanent methods of contraception work. Give one example of each method.
5. What is a **spermicide?** What other methods of contraception should be used with a spermicide?

Health at School

Comparing Contraceptives Create a poster that compares five of the contraceptive methods you learned about in this chapter. Include abstinence as one of the five methods compared. Be sure to include each method's effectiveness and its ability to prevent the spread of STIs. WRITING

Critical Thinking

6. **Applying Concepts** What is the only method of contraception that also offers some protection against STIs?
7. **Comparing and Contrasting** Compare the pros and cons of barrier methods and hormonal methods.

Section 4 Review

1. Abstinence eliminates the possibility that an egg and sperm could come into contact; it also eliminates the possibility of physical contact that could transmit STIs.
2. whether a prescription is needed; planning and preparation that is needed; side effects or health risks; whether it protects against STIs; how effective it is at preventing pregnancy
3. Effectiveness refers to the likelihood that using the method will prevent pregnancy.
4. Barrier methods prevent sperm from reaching an egg, e.g., a male condom. Hormonal methods prevent ovulation or inhibit fertilization, e.g., the pill. Permanent methods make a person incapable of reproduction, e.g., vasectomy.
5. A spermicide is a chemical that kills sperm; diaphragms, cervical caps, and shields.
6. Condoms provide some protection against STIs.
7. *Sample answer:* A pro of barrier methods is that you only have to use the method when you participate in intercourse. A pro of hormonal methods is that they are more effective at preventing pregnancy than barrier methods.

Chapter 4 Review

VIDEO **TEENS Talk**
Teen Pregnancy Describe how pregnancy affected the long-term plans of the teens in the video.

Reviewing Key Ideas

Section 1

1. Which of the following is NOT a part of a successful marriage?
   a. compatibility
   b. compromise
   c. perfectionism
   d. communication
2. Explain the importance of commitment in a successful marriage.
3. Describe two big challenges most married teenagers face.
4. **Critical Thinking** Discuss at least three factors that a couple should consider before they decide to be parents.

Section 2

5. During implantation
   a. the egg is fertilized.
   b. the blastocyst travels to the uterus.
   c. the blastocyst attaches to the wall of the uterus.
   d. the embryo grows to about an inch in length.
6. Describe how a fetus obtains nutrients and gets rid of wastes.
7. What changes occur in a fetus between the seventh and ninth month of development?
8. **Critical Thinking** Why do you think many expectant parents keep pregnancy a secret until after the first trimester?

Section 3

9. Which nutrient is critical for proper neural tube development?
   a. iron
   b. folic acid
   c. sodium
   d. vitamin A
10. List four environmental hazards of particular concern to pregnant women.
11. During which trimester of a pregnancy should a woman start prenatal care?
12. **Critical Thinking** Why do you think that many pregnant teens do not receive proper medical care during the first trimester?

Section 4

13. Which contraceptive method is most effective in preventing pregnancy and avoiding the transmission of STIs?
    a. a female condom
    b. a diaphragm
    c. oral contraception
    d. a male condom
14. List three benefits of sexual abstinence.
15. How does the combination pill prevent pregnancy?
16. Explain why withdrawal is an unreliable method of birth control.
17. **Critical Thinking** Why do you think that the use of alcohol or other drugs leads to many unplanned pregnancies?

Building Health Skills

18. **Advocacy** How could you help an older cousin stop smoking before she decides to have a baby?
19. **Making Decisions** Suppose you were recently married, but did not want to have children for several years. What factors would you consider when deciding how to delay parenthood?
20. **Setting Goals** Identify one habit you could change that would help you be a better parent in your 20s or 30s. It may seem a long way off, but changing habits is easiest when you are young. Write down the habit you would like to change, and monitor your progress over the school year.

Health and Community

Folic Acid Awareness Many health organizations recommend that all women increase their folic acid consumption, starting in their teen years. Create a public service announcement to deliver this important message to teenage girls. In it, describe the importance of folic acid and offer tips for adding more of it to one's diet. **WRITING**

Chapter 4 Review

Section 1

1. c
2. Commitment is the determination to have a fulfilling lifelong marriage.
3. *Sample answer:* Most married teenagers have difficulty supporting themselves financially, and they may lose friends because of different interests and goals.
4. *Sample answer:* Whether they are financially ready to have a child, who will take care of the child, whether they are emotionally ready.

Section 2

5. c
6. Blood vessels in the umbilical cord carry nutrients from the placenta to the embryo and wastes from the embryo to the placenta.
7. The body size of the fetus increases in relation to the head, body fat accumulates, and the eyelids open and close.
8. *Sample answer:* Most miscarriages occur during the first trimester.

Section 3

9. b
10. X-rays, lead, mercury, cat litter
11. the first trimester
12. *Sample answer:* Pregnant teens may not realize they are pregnant in the first trimester.

Section 4

13. d
14. *Sample answer:* It eliminates worry about pregnancy or STIs, allows for focus on achieving current goals, and enables the development of an emotionally intimate relationship.
15. The combination pill prevents ovulation.
16. Withdrawal is unreliable because a male does not always have the self-control to withdraw before ejaculation, and some fluid containing sperm may be released before ejaculation.
17. *Sample answer:* Alcohol and other drugs can lower inhibitions, which could lead to unprotected sex.

Building Health Skills

18. *Sample answer:* I could explain how smoking harms a developing baby and offer my support to help her quit.
19. I would consider the pros and cons of different contraceptive methods, including cost, convenience, and health risks.
20. Students can pick any habit that might interfere with being a good parent or having a healthy pregnancy later in life.

Health and Community

Folic Acid Awareness Student PSAs should include information about why folic acid is important for women of child-bearing age. They should also include a list of good nutritional sources of folic acid, such as green, leafy vegetables and legumes.

CHAPTER 5

Chapter Preview

Section 1 The Risks of Sexual Activity
Several risky behaviors account for the current epidemic of sexually transmitted infections (STIs), including ignoring the risks of sexual activity. Practicing sexual abstinence is the best way to avoid STIs.

Section 2 Kinds of STIs
Three of the most common STIs in the United States are trichomoniasis, human papilloma virus, and chlamydia. Other STIs include hepatitis, gonorrhea, genital herpes, and syphilis. Individuals who think they may be infected with an STI should seek prompt medical attention.

Section 3 HIV and AIDS
HIV attacks specific cells of the immune system. When the immune system becomes severely disabled, the infected person has AIDS. Individuals infected with HIV can pass the virus on to someone else through the exchange of blood or other body fluids. HIV and AIDS are global health problems.

Section 4 Protecting Yourself From HIV and AIDS
You can protect yourself from HIV by practicing abstinence, avoiding drugs, and avoiding contact with others' blood and body fluids. In an HIV test, a person's blood is tested for antibodies to HIV. The main goal of HIV treatment is to keep the person's immune system functioning as normally as possible.

National Health Education Standards Correlation

1.12.1, 1.12.8, 1.12.9, 3.12.1, 3.12.2, 3.12.4, 4.12.2, 7.12.2, 8.12.3, 8.12.4

GO ONLINE
PearsonSuccessNet.com
For resources and activities for this chapter.

CHAPTER 5

Sexually Transmitted Infections and AIDS

GO ONLINE PearsonSuccessNet.com

TEENS Talk

Risks and STIs

Preview **Activity**

How Risky Is Sexual Activity?

Complete this activity before you watch the video.

1. Complete each of the following statements by filling in the blank.
   a. Being sexually active as a teen is __?__.
   b. There are __?__ risks that come with sexual activity.
   c. A person should not be sexually active until __?__.

2. Look over your responses. In a paragraph, summarize what you learned about your self by completing the statements. **WRITING**

Sensitive Issues

- Sexually transmitted infections and AIDS are likely to be sensitive issues for many students because of their association with sexual activity, particularly early sexual activity, and sexual activity with multiple partners. Students may be hesitant to discuss or ask questions about the issues for fear of appearing either too naive or too experienced in front of their peers. Give students the option of doing written activities instead of participating in classroom discussions.
- Be sure to stress the seriousness of STIs to the class. Make sure students realize that some STIs can cause lifelong illness, permanent infertility, and death.

87

VIDEO 22

TEENS Talk

Risks and STIs

Video Objectives

Use this video to help students

Identify the risks associated with sexual activity.

Explain why abstinence is the most effective strategy for avoiding STIs.

Practice abstinence to protect themselves from STIs.

Preview **Activity**

How Risky Is Sexual Activity?

Before watching the video, have students complete the Preview Activity by writing their answers in their private journals. After showing all three portions of the video, ask students to revisit their responses and make any changes they feel are necessary.

From the Authors

You may be wondering why we, as well as most public health professionals, have replaced the term *sexually transmitted disease (STD)* with the term *sexually transmitted infection (STI).* Using *STI* instead of *STD* allows inclusion of HIV infections (and not just AIDS, the disease) in the same category as sexually transmitted diseases. Using *STI* instead of *STD* also puts more emphasis on transmission and the fact that STIs are preventable. Prevention of STIs is the focus of many of the activities in this chapter. See, for example, the Health and Community activity on page 91 and the Connect to Your Life questions throughout the chapter.

ABILITY LEVELS

- **L1 For students with special needs**
- **L2 For less proficient readers**
- **L3 For all students**
- **L4 For gifted and talented students**
- **EL For English language learners**

Section 1

The Risks of Sexual Activity

Objectives
Before class begins, write the objectives on the board. Have students copy the objectives into their notebooks at the start of class.

1. Focus

Warm-Up **Quick**

Give students a few minutes to do the quiz. Then call on volunteers to read aloud their explanations. Make sure students understand that each statement is true. Discuss how thinking the statements are false might lead people to engage in risky behaviors.

Section 1

The Risks of Sexual Activity

Objectives

- **List** risky behaviors associated with the current epidemic of sexually transmitted infections.
- **Identify** the best way to avoid sexually transmitted infections during the teen years.

Vocabulary

- sexually transmitted infection (STI)
- monogamy

Warm-Up

Quick Quiz Which of these statements do you think are true? Which are false?

1. **It can take only one sexual contact with an infected person to get a sexually transmitted infection.**
2. **Even if you've been infected with a sexually transmitted infection before, you can get that same infection again.**
3. **You can have more than one sexually transmitted infection at a time.**
4. **You can get a sexually transmitted infection from sharing needles.**

WRITING For each of your responses, explain why you gave the answer you did. Review your answers after reading this section.

The Silent Epidemic

Any pathogen that spreads from one person to another during sexual contact is called a **sexually transmitted infection,** or **STI.** (Such infections are sometimes called sexually transmitted diseases, or STDs.) There are approximately 20 million new cases of STIs in the United States each year. Of those cases, about half occur in people between the ages of 15 and 24.

Harmful Effects of STIs The STI epidemic is a serious concern for several reasons. STIs are harmful in terms of physical and emotional suffering. And yearly healthcare expenses related to STIs in the United States amount to well over $10 billion.

In the short term, STIs may cause pain, discomfort, and embarrassment. The long-term consequences of STIs may include an increased risk of certain cancers and an increased risk of infertility in both men and women. Infertility is the condition of being unable to have children.

Many STIs can be treated with medicines, but some are incurable. If left untreated, some STIs are fatal. Unlike many other infectious diseases, people do not develop immunity to STIs after being infected. A person can be cured and then reinfected with the same STI again.

Sensitive Issues

Students who feel uncomfortable asking questions about sexually transmitted infections should have an opportunity to ask questions anonymously. At the end of class, have students hand in anonymous questions on slips of paper. In the next class, answer all serious, relevant questions.

MATH and Health

L3 Calculating Rates

Using Figure 1, have students calculate the average annual rate of increase in cases of chlamydia in 10- to 19-year-olds from 2006 to 2010. (Subtract the number of cases in 2006 from the number of cases in 2010, and divide the answer by 4 years; or, 90,000 cases ÷ 4 yr = 22,500 cases/yr.)

Challenge students to calculate the number of cases there would be in 2014 if this rate of increase continued. (Add 22,500 cases per year, times 4 years, to the number of cases in 2010; or, 450,000 cases + 90,000 cases = 540,000 cases.) Ask: **What assumption does this prediction make?** *(The rate of increase does not change.)*

Risky Behaviors and the STI Epidemic **There are several risky behaviors that account for the current STI epidemic, including ignoring the risks of sexual activity, having sexual contact with multiple partners, and not getting proper treatment when necessary.**

- **Ignoring Risks** Being sexually active puts a person at risk for STIs. Many people who are sexually active do not take precautions against infection. They often do not realize the risks of contracting STIs, or they choose to ignore the risks. Adolescents in particular tend to ignore the risks, thinking "It can't happen to me." But the reality is that it can, and it does happen to many teens.
- **Multiple Partners** Many people begin to engage in sexual activity at a young age, and some may have multiple sexual partners during their lifetimes. The more sexual partners a person has, the greater the chance of getting an STI.
- **Not Seeking Treatment** Some people who become infected do not seek immediate medical treatment. Sometimes people are too embarrassed to seek treatment. Others don't know that they have an STI because they do not recognize the symptoms. In some cases, STIs have no symptoms and can only be detected by laboratory tests. Sometimes the symptoms go away temporarily, leading the person to think the infection has been cured. In all of these situations, the infection may go untreated, increasing the chances that the person will spread it to others.

Connect to Your Life **What advice would you give a friend who seems to be ignoring the risks of sexual activity?**

GO ONLINE
PearsonSuccessNet.com
For: More on sexually transmitted infections

FIGURE 1 This graph shows data for one STI, chlamydia, that is common among young people. **Evaluating** Why do you think young people are especially at risk for STIs?

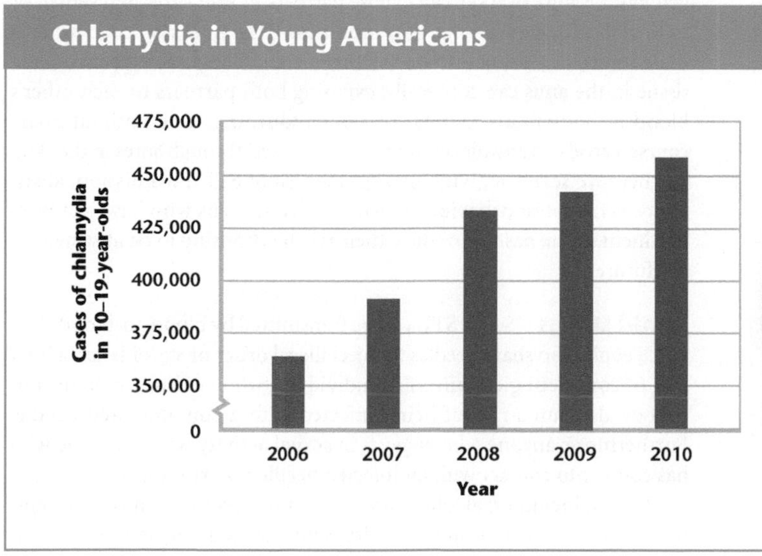

Differentiated Instruction

L2 Less Proficient Readers

Show students how to use the subheadings under "The Silent Epidemic" to create a concept map that can help them identify the main ideas in the passage. The basic concept map should show that the STI epidemic causes harmful effects and is caused by risky behaviors. Students should add details to the basic concept map, including specific harmful effects and risky behaviors. Suggest that students make concept maps whenever they need help identifying the main ideas in a passage.

2. Teach

The Silent Epidemic

L3 Content Update GO ONLINE

Visit Pearson SuccessNet to access more information about sexually transmitted infections. Have students complete the Web activity.

L2 Active Learning

Ask students to create posters about the harmful effects of STIs, using the information on page 88 as a starting point. Students' goal should be to impress observers with the seriousness of STIs. Arrange to display their posters throughout the school.

L3 Building Health Skills

Analyzing Influences Have students read about the risky behaviors that account for the current STI epidemic. Ask: **What factors might influence some young people to adopt these risky behaviors?** *(Sample answers: seeing sexual activity without consequences in the media; feeling peer pressure to become sexually active)* **How could you resist these influences?** *(Sample answers: learn about the risks of sexual activity; choose friends who practice sexual abstinence)*

L2 Visual Learning: Figure 1

Image Bank Figure 22-1

Introduce the graph in the figure by telling students that chlamydia is one of the most common STIs in the United States. Call on a volunteer to describe in words the trend shown in the graph. Discuss what young people should do if they think they have chlamydia. Call on students to answer the caption question.

Caption Answer *Sample answer:* Young people may be especially likely to ignore the risks of sexual activity, to have multiple sexual partners, and to not get proper treatment.

Connect to Your Life *Sample answer:* I would advise the friend to avoid sexual activity because of the risk of getting STIs.

Avoiding STIs

L3 Addressing Misconceptions

Teen Sexual Activity Teens often think that "everybody" they know is sexually active. Call on volunteers to estimate the percentage of teens in their grade who they think is sexually active. (Students are likely to overestimate the percentage of sexually active peers.) Share with students that recent studies show the majority of high school students have not had sex and choose to remain abstinent. Discuss why teens might talk more about sex than actually participate in it.

L2 Building Health Skills

Advocacy Have small groups of students write public service announcements in which they advocate sexual abstinence as a way to avoid STIs. Give groups a chance to share their announcements with the class. Make sure students understand that sexual abstinence applies to any activity in which blood or body fluids could be exchanged, not just to sexual intercourse. WRITING

L1 Cooperative Learning

Divide the class into pairs, and have each pair write a dialogue in which a teen resists pressure from another teen to try intravenous drugs. Dialogues should focus on refusing these drugs in order to avoid STIs. Have several pairs present their dialogues to the class, and ask other students to evaluate them. Discuss attributes of convincing refusals.

L3 Addressing Misconceptions

Barrier Protection and STIs Students may think that condoms can protect them from all STIs. Emphasize that condoms provide only limited protection against certain STIs. Tell students that genital herpes, syphilis, chancroid, and HPV (all of which are discussed in Section 2) can spread by skin-to-skin contact. Infected skin surfaces or sores may not be covered by a condom and therefore pose a risk for spreading the infection. Explain that this is why genital-to-genital touching is not necessarily a safe activity.

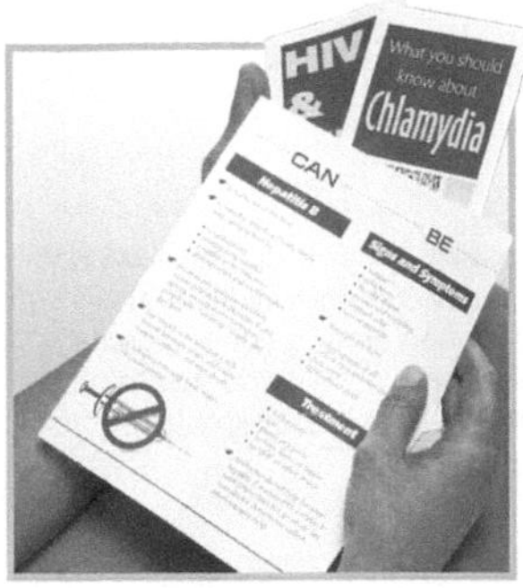

FIGURE 2 Educating yourself about STIs can help you make healthy decisions.

Avoiding STIs

STIs are transmitted mainly through sexual contact, but a few are also transmitted through contact with the blood of an infected person. **In the teen years, the best way to avoid STIs is to practice sexual abstinence and avoid drug abuse and other behaviors that may lead to exposure to infected blood or body fluids.**

Practice Abstinence The most certain way to avoid STIs is to practice sexual abstinence. Sexual abstinence means not engaging in sexual activity. Sexual activity such as oral sex, anal sex, genital-to-genital touching, and intercourse can transmit STIs.

Oral sex is contact between a person's mouth and another person's genitals. Because oral sex can expose partners to skin sores and semen or vaginal fluids, there is a risk of transmitting STIs. Anal sex occurs when a male inserts his penis into his partner's anus. This is risky because the tissue in the anus can tear easily, exposing both partners to each other's blood or body fluids. Genital-to-genital touching, even without intercourse, can also transmit certain STIs that spread through sores in the skin.

Because sexual activity involves the risk of STI transmission, abstinence is the safest behavior for avoiding STIs. Teens who have not been abstinent in the past can reduce their risk by choosing to be abstinent in the future.

Avoid Drugs Some STIs can be transmitted by blood-to-blood contact. People who share needles to inject illegal drugs or steroids run a high risk of contracting certain STIs. Individuals who get body piercings or tattoos also run a risk of being infected with a contaminated needle. Furthermore, anyone who engages in sexual activity with someone who has come into contact with an infected needle is at risk for STIs.

Drugs, including alcohol, also play an indirect role in the STI epidemic. Because alcohol and other drugs impair the ability to think clearly, people may make decisions they later regret.

TEENS *Are Asking . . .*

Q: My boyfriend is pressuring me to have sex, but I want to wait until marriage. How can I resist the pressure?

A: Congratulations on your healthy decision to remain abstinent! These tips may help you resist the pressure.

- Set specific goals. Know the line you will not cross, and review it often. Ask a friend to hold you accountable.
- State your boundaries. Make sure your boyfriend knows your limits. State them clearly at the start of the relationship.
- Put it in writing. Write a journal entry explaining your decision. This will help strengthen your commitment.
- Find supportive friends. Hang out with other teens who want to remain abstinent. They will support your decision.

Choose Responsible Friends A good way to ensure that you practice abstinence and avoid drugs is to choose friends who have also chosen those behaviors. Friends who support your healthy decisions can make it easier to resist the pressure to use drugs or engage in sexual behavior.

Sexual Fidelity Sexual fidelity, also called **monogamy,** means that two people have sexual contact only with one another. In a monogamous relationship, such as a marriage in which both partners are uninfected and are faithful to each other, there is little concern about STIs. Teens, however, should *not* count on sexual fidelity to protect them from STIs. This is because teen relationships are typically not stable or long lasting, although they might seem so at the time.

FIGURE 3 Choosing friends and activities that encourage abstinence can greatly reduce your risk of becoming infected with an STI.

Barrier Protection For people who are sexually active, but not in a monogamous relationship, the best way to reduce the risk of infection is to use a condom during every sexual encounter. A condom is a latex or polyurethane sheath that covers the penis. When used correctly, it acts as a physical barrier against many STIs. However, condoms do not provide 100% protection against any STI, and they do not provide any protection at all against some STIs. For example, some STIs can be spread by skin sores that are not covered by a condom. Or a condom could break during sexual activity. Abstinence remains the best protection against STIs.

Section 1 Review

Key Ideas and Vocabulary

1. What is a **sexually transmitted infection?**
2. What are three risky behaviors that contribute to the current STI epidemic?
3. Explain how practicing abstinence, avoiding drugs, and your choice of friends can help you avoid STIs.
4. What is **monogamy?** How is it helpful in protecting against STIs?

Critical Thinking

5. **Relating Cause and Effect** How is the fact that some STIs have few or no symptoms related to the STI epidemic?
6. **Evaluating** Explain how refusal skills and effective communication are important skills that teens can use to avoid STIs.
7. **Applying Concepts** Describe how someone would most effectively avoid STIs throughout their lifetime.

Health at School

STI Education Create a poster or a web page to educate teens about the risks of sexual activity and STIs. Include statistics about the incidence of STIs in teens. Include other facts that you think teens should be aware of. **WRITING**

3. Assess

Evaluate

These assignments can help you assess students' mastery of the section content.

L3 Section 1 Review

Answers appear below.

L2 Reteach

Work with students to make an outline of section content. Begin the outline with the major headings in the section, and leave room for students to add subheadings and important details. Have students work with partners to complete the outline. Suggest that students use their completed outlines when they review section content.

L4 Enrich

Health and Community

STI Education Students can use just the facts in the text, or they can include additional facts from other sources. Check that any additional facts are reliable, up-to-date, and relevant to teens. Posters and Web pages should be attractive, informative, and persuasive.

Section 1 Review

1. any pathogen that spreads from one person to another during sexual contact
2. ignoring risks of being sexually active, engaging in sexual activity with multiple partners, not seeking treatment for STIs
3. Sexual abstinence is the best way to avoid STIs. Avoiding drugs helps one avoid STIs because some STIs can be transmitted by sharing drug needles and because alcohol and other drugs make people more likely to engage in risky behaviors. Friends who support your healthy decisions can help you avoid STIs by making it easier to resist pressure to use drugs or engage in sexual activity.
4. Monogamy is when two people have sexual contact only with one another. Having contact with only one person's blood and body fluids can protect against STIs if both partners are uninfected.
5. People who have few or no symptoms are unlikely to seek medical attention or protect partners from infection.
6. Refusal skills and effective communication are important skills for resisting peer pressure to be sexually active and use drugs.
7. *Sample answer:* Practicing abstinence until marriage and then practicing sexual fidelity in marriage can provide protection against STIs throughout life.

Section 2

Kinds of STIs

Objectives
Before class begins, write the objectives on the board. Have students copy the objectives into their notebooks at the start of class.

1. Focus

Warm-Up Myth/Fact

Call on a few students to read their answers. Try to get a diversity of views. Some students might think that all STIs can be cured. Make sure students realize that some STIs infect people for life. Tell students they will learn about different kinds of STIs in this section, including those that can be cured and those that cannot.

Section 2

Kinds of STIs

Objectives

- **Identify** three of the most common STIs, including their symptoms and treatments.
- **List** four other STIs and describe their symptoms.
- **Know** when a person should seek treatment for an STI.

Vocabulary

- trichomoniasis
- urethritis
- vaginitis
- human papilloma virus
- chlamydia
- pelvic inflammatory disease
- gonorrhea
- genital herpes
- syphilis
- chancre

Warm-Up

Myth **All STIs can be treated with antibiotics.**

Fact **STIs caused by viruses cannot be treated with antibiotics. Antibiotics are only used to treat STIs caused by bacteria. Several STIs caused by viruses cannot be cured and can cause lifelong health problems.**

WRITING Do you think most teens are aware that some STIs are not easily treated? And that some may persist for years? Explain your answer.

The Most Common STIs

Like other infectious diseases you have learned about, STIs are caused by pathogens, including bacteria, viruses, and protozoans. The pathogens that cause STIs live in the reproductive organs of males and females. Some also live in the blood. STIs can be spread from person to person through blood and body fluids such as semen, vaginal secretions, and breast milk.

Early diagnosis and treatment of STIs is essential in preventing long-term health problems. Although some STIs do not have obvious symptoms, many do have distinct symptoms. Anyone experiencing symptoms of an STI should see a doctor immediately.

Three of the most common STIs in the United States are trichomoniasis, human papilloma virus, and chlamydia. It is important to be able to recognize the symptoms of these infections.

Trichomoniasis The STI known as **trichomoniasis** (trik uh moh NY uh sis) is caused by a protozoan that infects the urinary tract or vagina. In males, symptoms include painful urination, a clear discharge from the penis, and some itching. Most males experience no symptoms at all. Symptoms in females include itching and burning in the vagina, an unpleasant-smelling, yellowish discharge, and pain when urinating.

A doctor can prescribe medicine to cure a trichomoniasis infection. In males, if trichomoniasis is not treated, it can lead to inflammation of the lining of the urethra, called **urethritis** (yoor uh THRY tis). In females, untreated trichomoniasis can lead to **vaginitis** (vaj uh NY tis), which is a vaginal infection or irritation.

Sensitive Issues

Joking can be a defense mechanism for dealing with sensitive issues. Curb any joking behavior about STIs because joking can reinforce misconceptions and make issues seem less serious than they are. Stress that STIs are very serious and nothing to laugh about.

WRITING and Health

L3 Persuasive Letter
Have students suppose that a sexually active friend has developed painful urination and a clear discharge from the penis. He is reluctant to tell his parents about his problem and wants advice. Ask students to write a letter in which they try to persuade the friend to make the best choice for his health. (In their letters, students should try to convince the friend to see a doctor immediately because he might have an STI. They also might warn the friend to stop all sexual activity so as not to spread the infection.)

Human Papilloma Virus The most common viral STI in the United States is caused by the **human papilloma virus** (pap uh LOH muh), or HPV. In many cases, HPV causes no symptoms, so people may not be aware that they are infected.

Some forms of HPV cause genital warts, which may itch or burn. A doctor can remove the warts, but they may reappear. Sometimes, the body's immune system will destroy the virus, clearing the body of infection. But in some people, HPV remains in the body for life.

One of the most serious conditions associated with HPV infection is cervical cancer in women. Having regular Pap tests can help detect this type of cancer before it becomes life threatening.

Chlamydia The most common STI caused by bacteria in the United States is **chlamydia** (kluh MID ee uh). People who are sexually active should be checked regularly for chlamydia. The infection can be cured with antibiotics.

Infected males often experience painful, frequent urination and discharge from the penis. If untreated, chlamydia may lead to urethritis.

In females, chlamydia often has no symptoms other than a yellowish vaginal discharge. If untreated, chlamydia can cause a serious infection of the reproductive organs called **pelvic inflammatory disease,** or PID. PID can lead to infertility or an ectopic pregnancy, a potentially fatal condition where a fertilized egg implants somewhere other than in the uterus. In addition, a pregnant woman can transmit chlamydia to her baby during birth. If an infected infant survives, it may suffer damage to the lungs or eyes.

GO ONLINE
PearsonSuccessNet.com
For: More on sexually transmitted infections

Connect to Your Life **For each STI, list the symptoms that a person needs to watch for.**

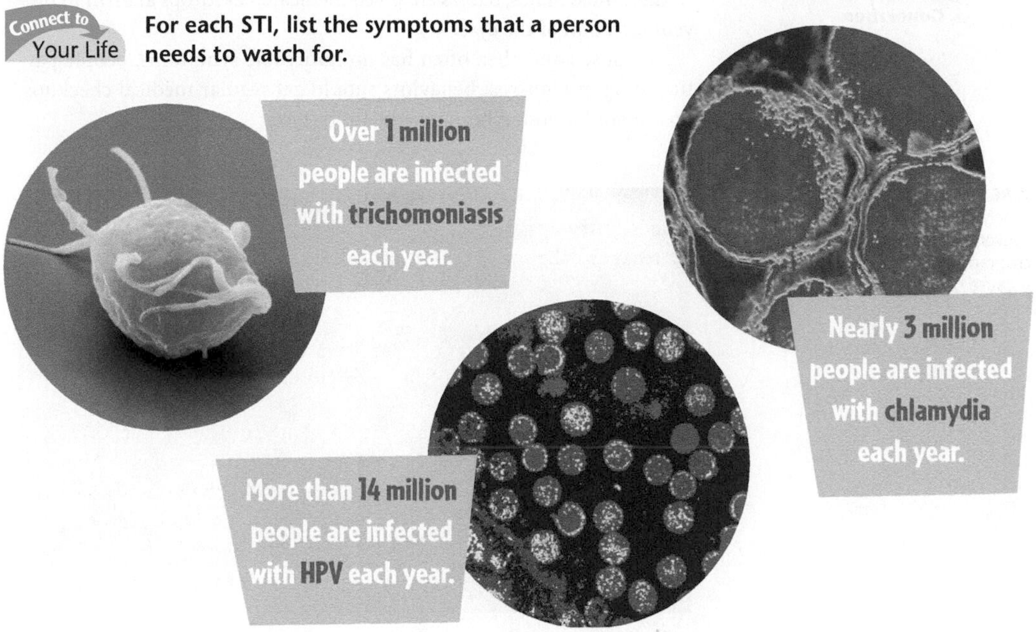

FIGURE 4 The micrographs show the pathogens that cause trichomoniasis, HPV, and chlamydia. These STIs affect millions of Americans every year.

2. Teach

The Most Common STIs

L3 Online Activity GO ONLINE

Visit Pearson SuccessNet to access an online activity about sexually transmitted infections. Have students complete the Web activity.

L3 Building Media Literacy

Ask students to come up with criteria to assess media sources for different types of STI information. Ask: **What would be important if you were looking for the most recent statistics on trichomoniasis?** *(how up-to-date the source is)* **If you wanted to know what genital warts look like?** *(whether the source has illustrations)* **If you wanted to know which antibiotic is used to treat chlamydia?** *(whether the source was written or reviewed by a doctor)*

L2 Building Vocabulary

Explain that the suffix *-itis* means "inflammation of" and that symptoms of inflammation can include itching, pain, and swelling. Ask: **What structures are inflamed in urethritis and vaginitis?** *(urethra and vagina, respectively)* **What are some other conditions that end in -itis?** *(Sample answers: tonsillitis, appendicitis, tendonitis)* In each condition, ask students to identify what structure is inflamed.

Connect to Your Life Symptoms of trichomoniasis in females include itching and burning in the vagina, yellowish discharge, and painful urination. Males might experience painful urination, a clear discharge from the penis, and itching. HPV often causes no symptoms, but some forms of HPV cause genital warts, which may itch or burn. Symptoms of chlamydia in males include painful, frequent urination and discharge from the penis. Females often have no symptoms other than a yellowish vaginal discharge.

Differentiated Instruction

EL English Language Learners

The names of STIs in this section may be difficult for English language learners to pronounce. Point out the phonetic spellings of these terms in the text. Read the terms aloud, being careful to pronounce them correctly. Ask students to say each term aloud a few times after you read it.

L4 Gifted and Talented

Challenge interested students to learn more about one of the three most common STIs from reliable online or library resources. Make sure all three STIs are covered by different students. Invite students to share what they learn with the class in an oral report.

Other STIs

L3 Class Discussion

Have students read about hepatitis in the text. Ask: **Why do you think people with hepatitis B or C are often unaware of their infection?** *(Most of the symptoms of hepatitis can also be caused by other illnesses, such as flu or food poisoning.)* **Why are new cases of hepatitis B, but not hepatitis C, likely to decline in the future?** *(Children are now routinely vaccinated against hepatitis B, but there is no vaccine for hepatitis C.)*

L3 Cultural Connection

Discuss how different cultures have different attitudes toward sex. However, most are somewhat reluctant to talk seriously about sex and its consequences. For example, some aspects of American culture are very open about sex, yet many Americans have limited knowledge about the risks of STIs. Challenge students to think of examples in American culture and other cultures that illustrate this dichotomy. Ask: **How might the reluctance to talk about the risks of sexual activity affect the STI epidemic?**

Other STIs

Other STIs can also cause health problems and require medical treatment. Information about some of these STIs is summarized in Figure 6. **Other STIs include hepatitis, gonorrhea, genital herpes, and syphilis.**

Hepatitis Hepatitis B and C, also called HBV and HCV, are sexually transmitted infections that attack the liver. They are also spread by blood-to-blood contact, such as when people share needles.

Individuals with HBV or HCV are often unaware of their infection. The most common symptoms are fatigue, abdominal pain, nausea, and jaundice. Both infections may lead to liver cancer or cirrhosis (sih ROH sis), a condition in which normal liver tissue is replaced by scar tissue.

Hepatitis B and C can be diagnosed by a blood test. Medications may relieve symptoms, but there is no cure for HBV or HCV. Children are now routinely vaccinated against HBV. Currently, there is no vaccine for HCV.

Gonorrhea A bacterial STI that infects the urinary tract of males and females and the reproductive organs of females is **gonorrhea** (gahn uh REE uh). Researchers estimate that about 820,000 Americans are infected with gonorrhea each year. Males usually have a thick, puslike discharge from the penis and painful urination. Females sometimes experience painful urination and a puslike discharge from the vagina or urinary tract. More often, however, symptoms in a woman are very mild and may not be noticed. If left untreated, gonorrhea can lead to urethritis and infertility in males. In females it may lead to PID and infertility.

An infected woman can transmit gonorrhea to her baby during birth. In the United States, babies are given medicated eyedrops at birth to prevent infection of the eyes.

Because gonorrhea often has no noticeable symptoms, people participating in high-risk behaviors should get regular medical checkups. Treatment for gonorrhea requires antibiotics.

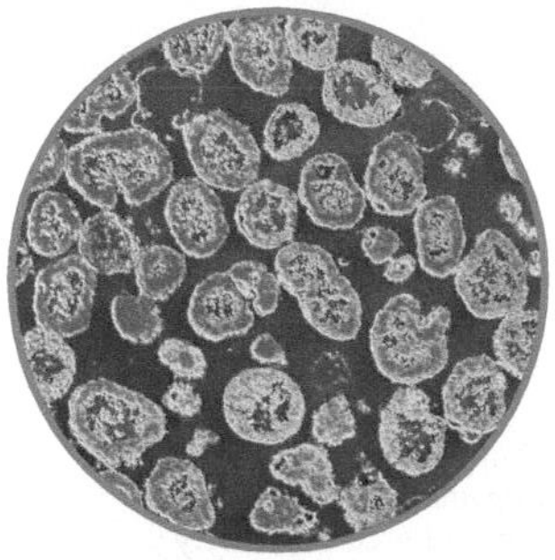

▲ **Gonorrhea**

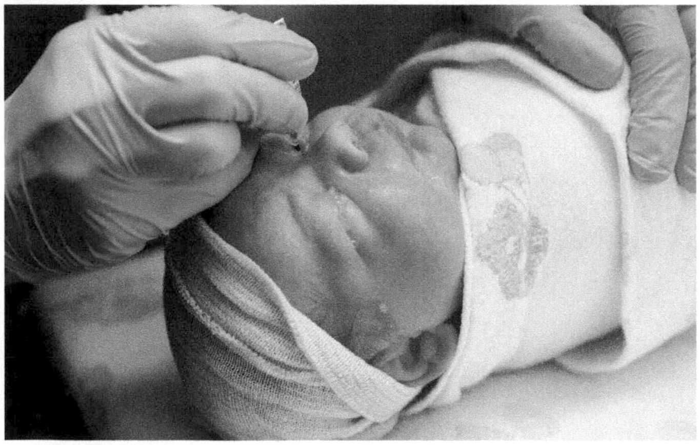

FIGURE 5 Newborn babies are routinely given medicated eyedrops to prevent gonorrhea infection. The micrograph above shows the bacteria that cause gonorrhea.

For Your INFORMATION!

STIs in Teens

In 2005, the American Social Health Association (ASHA) reported the following facts about STIs in American teens.

- Half of sexually active youth become infected with an STI by the age of 25.
- Half of all new HIV cases occur in teens.
- Less than half of teens talk about STIs with their doctor.

In the same report, ASHA made the following recommendations.

- There should be better communication about STIs between teens and parents and between teens and healthcare providers.
- Teens should be educated about STI risks and prevention.

As a health teacher, you can help implement both recommendations. You can give students opportunities to improve their communication skills and teach them about STI risks and prevention.

FIGURE 6 Chancroid, bacterial vaginosis, pubic lice, and scabies are all treatable STIs. **Classifying** Which of these STIs can affect both males and females?

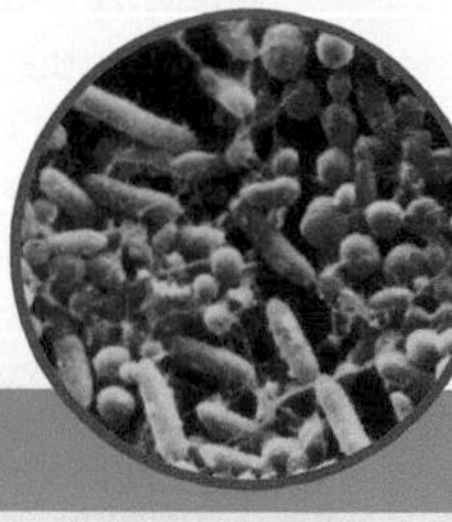

◀ Chancroid

Other STIs

Infection	Pathogen	Symptoms	How Spread	Treatment
Chancroid	Bacteria	Painful sores around the genitals	Contact with sores	Antibiotics
Bacterial vaginosis	Bacteria	In women, discharge, pain, itching, or burning in or around the vagina	Role of sexual activity in the spread of bacterial vaginosis is unclear	Antibiotics
Pubic lice and Scabies	Insects and mites that infest the hair around the genitals	Itching around the genitals; a rash	Direct physical contact with an infested person or with infested clothing or bedding	Medicated shampoo; washing infested clothing or bedding in very hot water

▲ Pubic louse

Genital Herpes Another STI caused by a virus is **genital herpes** (HUR peez). The virus that causes genital herpes is the herpes simplex virus. Researchers estimate that one out of six people aged 14 to 49 is infected with a herpes simplex virus.

In some people, the symptoms may be hardly noticeable, and they may not realize they are infected. In other people, symptoms may be more severe, including painful blisters that appear on or around the genitals. A doctor can prescribe medicine to relieve the discomfort and dry up the blisters, but there is no cure for genital herpes. Infected people can experience periodic outbreaks of blisters throughout their lives.

An infected individual can pass the herpes simplex virus to a sexual partner whether blisters are present or not. A woman with genital herpes can infect her infant during childbirth, causing blindness and possibly death. A doctor may recommend that an infected woman have a cesarean section to prevent the baby from being infected.

Connect to Your Life **If a friend were considering a body piercing, what would you say about the risk of hepatitis?**

L2 Visual Learning: Figure 6

Have students read about the other STIs in the table. Challenge students to brainstorm how each of the STIs could be prevented. (Students' responses should make it clear that abstinence is the only certain way to avoid infection with each STI.) Make sure students realize that avoiding infested clothing and bedding is also important for preventing infections of pubic lice and scabies.
Caption Answer: chancroid, pubic lice, and scabies

L3 Journal Writing

Ask students to imagine what it would be like to have genital herpes. Remind them that there is no cure for this viral STI and that infected people may have periodic outbreaks of painful blisters throughout their lives. Have students consider how this would affect their health, relationships, and happiness. Ask students to address these questions in a confidential journal entry. Writing about possible lifelong negative consequences of sexual activity should reinforce the importance of practicing abstinence now. **WRITING**

Connect to Your Life *Sample answer:* There is a risk of contracting hepatitis from contaminated piercing needles. Hepatitis is an incurable disease that can lead to liver cancer and cirrhosis.

Differentiated Instruction

L1 Special Needs

Pair special needs students with more proficient students, and ask pairs to make a table, modeled on Figure 6, comparing and contrasting hepatitis, gonorrhea, and genital herpes. For each STI, they should include the type of pathogen, symptoms, how the infection is spread, and treatment. Organizing what they read in a compare/contrast table will help students focus on the most important information in the passage.

L2 Cooperative Learning

Divide the class into small groups, and have students design a survey for other teens to see how familiar they are with each of the STIs described in the text. Students should design their surveys so as to determine how much teens know about each disease, such as how the disease is transmitted, what symptoms it causes, and whether it can be cured. If time allows, have students use their surveys to assess the knowledge of other students at their school. Ask students to share the results of their surveys. Ask: **How can lack of knowledge about STIs increase the risk of infection?**

L3 Building Health Skills

Accessing Information Ask students where they could learn about several different aspects of syphilis, including the origin of the term (e.g., dictionary), current statistics on the prevalence of the disease (e.g., government Web site), and usual treatment (e.g., medical reference book). Discuss how different types of information about the same topic may require accessing different kinds of sources.

Seeking Treatment

L3 Active Learning

Ask small groups of students to contact their state or local health department or the Centers for Disease Control and Prevention to learn about clinics in their community that test for STIs. They should find out about clinic costs, policies regarding patient confidentiality, and clinic contact information. Ask groups to compile what they learn in a pamphlet. Display their pamphlets in the classroom.

Syphilis Although far less common than it used to be, thousands of people in the United States become infected with syphilis each year. **Syphilis** (SIF uh lis) is a serious bacterial STI that progresses through three distinct stages.

- In the first stage, a painless sore called a **chancre** (SHANG kur) appears at the site of exposure. The bacteria may spread from the sore to different parts of the body.
- In the second stage, sores appear in the mouth and flulike symptoms develop. A nonitchy skin rash often appears on the hands and feet.
- In the third stage, symptoms may disappear for years. During this time, however, the bacteria attack internal parts of the body, such as the brain and heart. Eventually, untreated syphilis can cause brain damage, paralysis, and heart disease. This damage can lead to death.

In its early stages, syphilis can be treated and cured with antibiotics. Once it progresses beyond the second stage, the bacteria can be killed, but any damage that has already occurred is permanent.

A pregnant woman with syphilis will pass the disease to her developing baby. If the mother does not receive treatment during pregnancy, syphilis can damage the baby's skin, bones, eyes, teeth, and liver. A baby born with syphilis is said to have congenital syphilis.

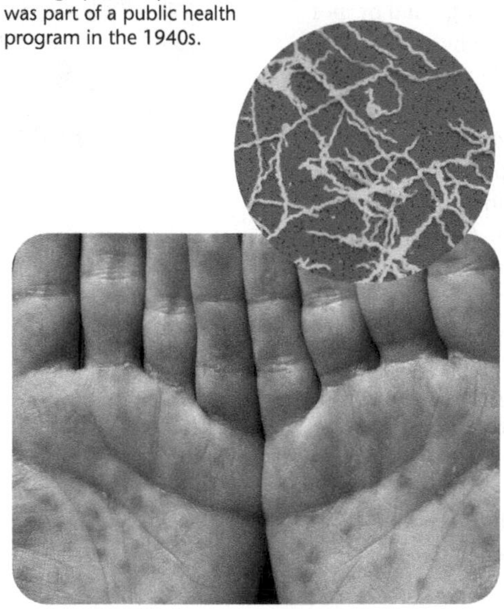

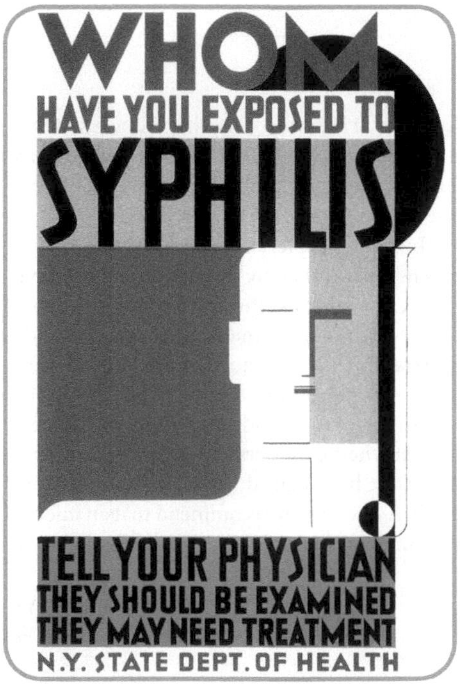

FIGURE 7 An itchless rash on the hands is one of the symptoms of syphilis. The bacteria that cause syphilis are spiral-shaped, as you can see in the micrograph. The poster shown here was part of a public health program in the 1940s.

TEENS *Are Asking . . .*

Q: I'm abstinent now, but I was sexually active on one occasion in the past. I had a rash after that one time, and I was worried that I might have an STI. Then the rash went away, so I figured it was nothing. Was I right?

A: The fact that your rash went away is no guarantee that you are free of infection. STIs may cause no symptoms or cause only temporary symptoms. For example, gonorrhea often causes no noticeable symptoms in females, and the initial symptoms of syphilis usually go away after a short time. There is significant risk of infection, especially for females, with even one exposure to an STI. For example, 50 percent of females become infected with gonorrhea after one exposure. You should tell your doctor about your situation and get tested. If you do have an STI, you should be treated as soon as possible.

Seeking Treatment

Being tested for STIs may be uncomfortable and embarrassing, but it is crucial for long-term health. **People who participate in high-risk behaviors should get medical checkups every six months. Individuals who suspect they may be infected should seek prompt medical attention.**

A person who suspects an STI infection should refrain from sexual activity and see a doctor. Depending on the symptoms, the doctor may need to do a physical exam or a blood test. If an infection is present and treatable, the person should start treatment immediately. It is important to finish all of the prescribed medicine, even if symptoms disappear.

If a person finds out that he or she has an STI, it is also important to notify any sexual partners, so they can seek treatment as well. If the STI is not curable, the doctor can offer advice about how to live with the disease and how to prevent passing it on to others.

Many states have clinics that test for STIs. The results of these tests are confidential. Information about clinics that test for STIs is available from state or local public health departments or from the Centers for Disease Control and Prevention.

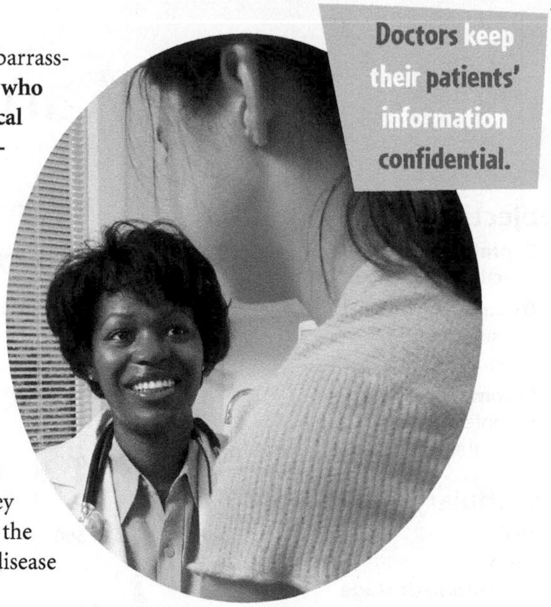

FIGURE 8 It is very important for long-term health to see a doctor if you think you might have an STI.

Section 2 Review

Key Ideas and Vocabulary

1. What are three of the most common STIs in the United States? What type of pathogen causes each STI?
2. Why is **pelvic inflammatory disease** a serious problem in women?
3. List the symptoms of hepatitis, gonorrhea, genital herpes, and syphilis.
4. Which stage of syphilis is characterized by the appearance of a **chancre**?
5. When should a person seek treatment for STIs?

Health at Home

Accessing STI Information Write down a list of questions that you have about STIs. Set up a time with a parent or other trusted adult to discuss your questions. If the person doesn't know the answers, ask for his or her help in finding the answers. WRITING

Critical Thinking

6. **Classifying** Which of the STIs that you learned about in this section can be treated but not cured? Which can be cured if treated early?
7. **Applying Concepts** Suppose a friend is worried about a possible STI. Write an e-mail to your friend, offering your advice about what to do. WRITING

3. Assess

Evaluate

These assignments can help you assess students' mastery of the section content.

L3 Section 2 Review

Answers appear below.

L2 Reteach

Have pairs of students play a quiz game in which one student chooses an STI and the partner asks three "yes" or "no" questions (e.g., Is it caused by a virus? Does it cause symptoms?) to try to identify which STI it is. Have partners alternate roles. Partners should play the game until they have covered all the STIs in the section. The partner who correctly identifies more STIs is the winner.

L4 Enrich

Health at Home

Accessing STI Information Suggest that students discuss their questions with a school nurse if they feel uncomfortable discussing them with a parent. If students cannot find answers to some of their questions, suggest possible sources of relevant information.

Section 2 Review

1. trichomoniasis (protozoan), human papilloma virus (virus), and chlamydia (bacteria)
2. PID can lead to infertility or an ectopic pregnancy, which is potentially fatal.
3. Hepatitis: fatigue, abdominal pain, nausea, and jaundice; gonorrhea: puslike discharge and painful urination; genital herpes: painful blisters on or around the genitals; syphilis: a painless sore at the site of exposure, sores in the mouth, flulike symptoms, a rash on the hands and feet, brain damage, paralysis, and heart disease.
4. the first stage
5. A person who participates in high-risk behaviors should get medical checkups every six months. A person who suspects he or she may be infected should seek prompt medical attention.
6. HPV, hepatitis B and C, and genital herpes can be treated but not cured. Trichomoniasis, chlamydia, gonorrhea, chancroid, bacterial vaginosis, pubic lice, scabies, and syphilis can be cured if treated early.
7. E-mails should urge the friend to be tested for STIs as soon as possible so treatment, if needed, can be started early.

Section 3

HIV and AIDS

Objectives
Before class begins, write the objectives on the board. Have students copy the objectives into their notebooks at the start of class.

1. Focus

***Warm-Up* Health Stats**

Call on volunteers to share what they wrote. Factors students identify might range from an increase in sexual activity in 13–24-year-olds to new drugs that help people with HIV and AIDS live longer. Tell students they will learn more about the trends in this section.

Section 3

HIV and AIDS

Objectives

- **Explain** how HIV infection leads to AIDS.
- **Describe** how HIV is transmitted from person to person.
- **Summarize** the state of HIV infection and AIDS throughout the world.

Vocabulary

- HIV
- AIDS
- asymptomatic stage
- opportunistic infection

Warm-Up

Health Stats What health trend does this graph reveal?

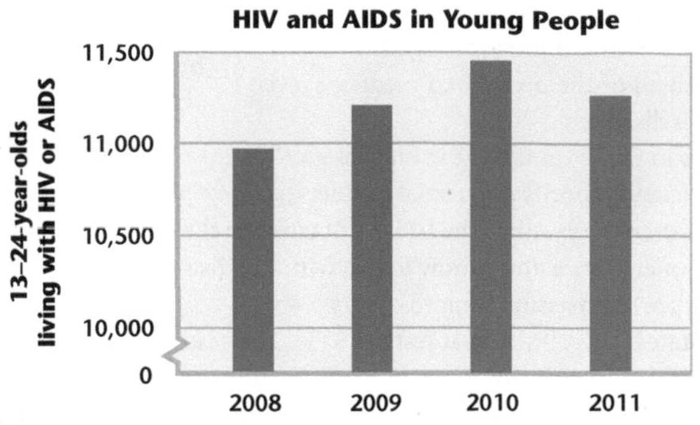

WRITING What factors might account for this trend?

HIV Infection

The most serious incurable STI is caused by the human immunodeficiency virus, commonly called **HIV.** As of 2011, 1.4 million Americans were reported to be living with HIV. And 13- to 24-year-olds account for approximately 13% of HIV cases reported in the United States.

HIV infection can lead to **AIDS,** or acquired immunodeficiency syndrome, which is an often fatal disease of the immune system. **HIV attacks specific cells of the immune system, disabling the body's defenses against other pathogens. When the immune system becomes severely disabled, the infected person has AIDS.**

How HIV Attacks the Immune System Inside the body, HIV infects helper T cells, which stimulate other cells of the immune system to produce antibodies against invading pathogens. Inside a helper T cell, HIV reproduces, killing the cell in the process. The new viruses are released from the cell and move on to destroy other helper T cells.

By counting the number of helper T cells that remain active in the body, the progression of HIV infection can be monitored. The fewer helper T cells, the more advanced the disease. Figure 9 shows how helper T cell counts can be used to monitor the progression of the disease.

Sensitive Issues

HIV and AIDS may be sensitive issues for students who have personal experiences with them. Be careful in the language you use when discussing the issues. For example, refer to AIDS patients as "people with AIDS," rather than as "victims of AIDS."

WRITING and Health

L3 Persuasive Letter

Have students find a local organization that supports people with HIV and AIDS and that needs volunteers. Then have students write a letter in which they try to convince a friend to volunteer for the organization. Letters should be informative and persuasive and provide information that makes it easy for the friend to get involved. Urge students to mail their letters and to get involved themselves.

Stages of HIV Infection HIV slowly destroys the immune system. Doctors describe HIV infection as progressing through three stages.

- **Asymptomatic Stage** Soon after exposure to HIV, an infected person may experience flulike symptoms, which usually go away after a few weeks. Many months or years may follow during which the person shows no outward signs of disease. Because of the lack of symptoms, this period is called the **asymptomatic stage.** During this stage, the virus destroys helper T cells. People in the asymptomatic stage can infect others even though they feel fine.
- **Symptomatic Stage** When an HIV-infected person starts to experience symptoms, he or she has entered the symptomatic stage of infection. Symptoms may include weight loss, a persistent fever, diarrhea, or fungal infections. Such symptoms may not appear until 7 to 10 years after infection with HIV.
- **AIDS** The onset of AIDS is usually marked by a very low number of helper T cells in the blood, as shown in Figure 9. At this stage, HIV-infected people are usually experiencing even more severe symptoms than in the symptomatic stage. Because the body's ability to fight disease has been weakened by HIV, they are susceptible to infections that a healthy person's immune system could easily fight off.

Connect to Your Life **Can you assume that someone who looks healthy is not infected with HIV? Explain.**

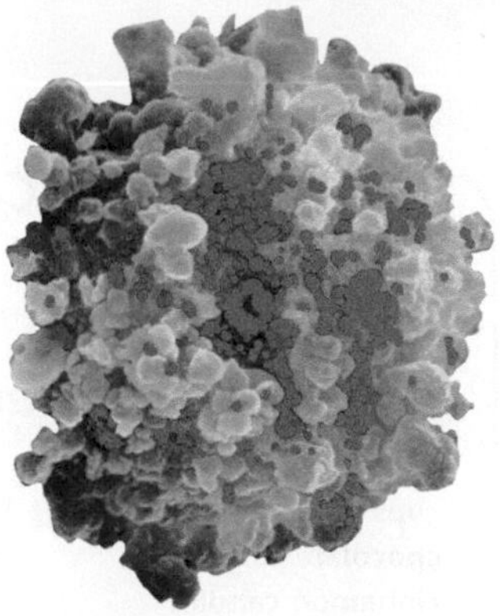

▲ **HIV viruses (red) emerging from a human helper T cell**

FIGURE 9 The number of helper T cells in the blood decreases as HIV infects and destroys more cells. **Reading Graphs** Describe how T cell counts change over time in a person infected with HIV.

T Cell Count and HIV Infection

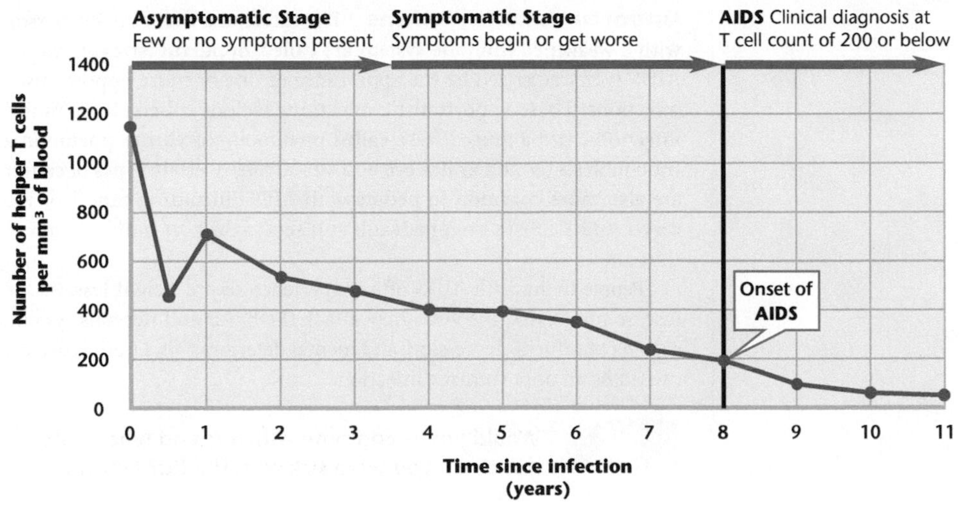

2. Teach

HIV Infection

L2 Addressing Misconceptions

HIV or AIDS? Many people are confused about the difference between HIV and AIDS. Make sure students understand that HIV refers to the virus that causes the infection and that AIDS is the disease caused by the virus. Ask: **How does HIV cause AIDS?** *(HIV attacks cells in the immune system so people cannot fight off infections.)* Point out that people may have HIV infections for many years before developing AIDS.

L3 Visual Learning: Figure 9

Image Bank Figure 22-9

Guide students in interpreting the graph. Ask: **At what level of helper T cells is AIDS diagnosed?** *(below 200 helper T cells per mm³ of blood)* **Based on the graph, about how long does it take AIDS to develop after infection with HIV?** *(about eight years)* Point out to students that this time can vary from person to person. Call on a volunteer to answer the caption question.

Caption Answer T cell counts decline sharply in the first six months after infection, rise somewhat in the second six months, and then show a steady, continuous decline for many years.

Connect to Your Life No, because the first stage of HIV infection is asymptomatic, meaning the person shows no outward signs of disease.

Differentiated Instruction

EL English Language Learners

There are many difficult terms in this lesson, including *immunodeficiency, asymptomatic,* and *opportunistic.* These and other terms may be obstacles for English language learners and discourage them from reading. In class, make sure that you correctly pronounce and clearly enunciate difficult terms. Have English language learners create flashcards of those terms, including pronunciations. Students should write the definitions of difficult terms in their own words on the flashcards.

Hands-On *Activity*

How Quickly Can HIV Spread?

You can use other items to represent HIV and non-HIV (such as two different types of dried beans), as long as they are distinct. At the start of the activity, fill one student's cup with only cinnamon candies to represent a single infected individual. Fill all the other students' cups with only chocolate candies to represent uninfected individuals.

Think and Discuss Answers

1. Answers will vary. The more partners students exchange candies with, the greater the number of students who will end up with cinnamon candy (HIV).
2. *Sample answer:* Having multiple sexual partners greatly increases the chances of getting infected with HIV or another STI.

L3 Building Media Literacy

Assign groups of students different types of health media (e.g., medical Web sites, health magazines, encyclopedias). Ask each group to search its type of media for a source about opportunistic infections and AIDS. Tell students to look for sources that are informative yet understandable by people without any special background knowledge. Ask groups to share their sources and discuss which type of health media seems most suitable for people without prior knowledge of a topic.

Connect to Your Life *Sample answer:* No, because a person who is HIV-positive might have a weakened immune system and be more susceptible to the flu.

Hands-On *Activity*

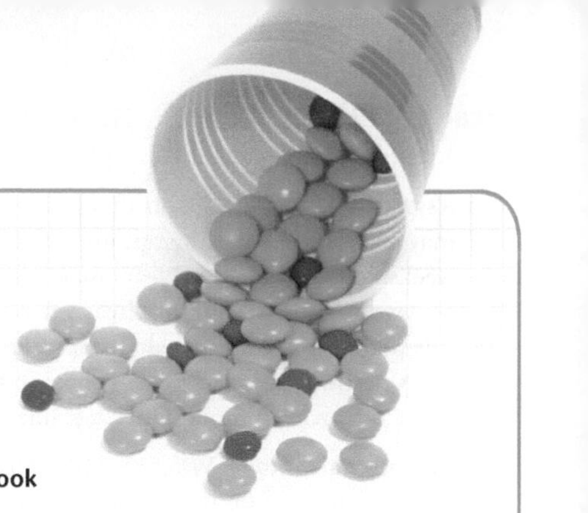

How Quickly Can HIV Spread?

Materials

cups
chocolate candies
cinnamon candies

Try This

1. Your teacher will give you a cup filled with small candies. Do not look inside the cup.
2. Walk around the room until your teacher tells you to stop. At that point, pair up with the student closest to you.
3. Pour a few of the candies from your cup into your partner's cup. Your partner should also pour some candies into your cup.
4. Repeat steps 2 and 3 two more times.
5. Look at the candies in your cup. If you have a cinnamon candy, you have been "infected" with HIV.

Think and Discuss

1. How many people in your class ended up with a cinnamon candy (HIV) in their cup? Would it surprise you to learn that only one person was infected to begin with?
2. Suppose that each person you exchanged candies with represents a sexual partner. How many people other than you did each of your partners exchange candies with? What does this suggest about having multiple sexual partners and the chances of getting infected with HIV or another STI?

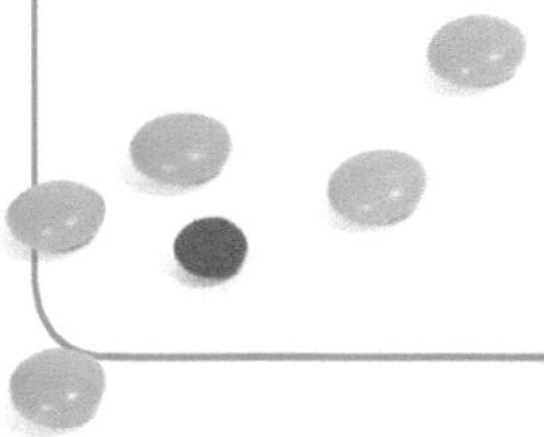

Opportunistic Infections The infections that attack a person with a weakened immune system are called **opportunistic infections.** AIDS is characterized by the appearance of one or more opportunistic infections. These opportunistic infections include tuberculosis, fungal infections, and a lung disease called pneumocystis carinii pneumonia (noo moh SIS tis kuh RY nee eye noo MOHN yuh). Certain types of cancer are also more common in people with AIDS, including cancer of the cervix and Kaposi's sarcoma (kuh POH seez sahr KOH muh), a kind of skin cancer.

People living with AIDS often experience severe weight loss. As the disease progresses, the virus may attack the brain and nervous system, causing blindness, depression, and mental deterioration. Death is usually caused by an opportunistic infection.

Connect to Your Life **Would you spend time with a friend who is HIV-positive if you were sick with the flu? Explain.**

For Your INFORMATION!

HIV Transmission Among Teens

HIV transmission is especially high among teens. One quarter of all new HIV cases in the United States is diagnosed in people age 20 or younger. The main modes of HIV transmission in teens are sexual contact and shared drug needles. The incidence of other STIs, such as chlamydia and genital herpes, is also high in teens, and this increases the risk of infection with HIV. This is because many STIs cause sores that provide portals through which HIV can enter the bloodstream.

Transmission of HIV

People with HIV are infectious whether or not they have any symptoms of disease. **Individuals infected with HIV can pass the virus on to someone else through the exchange of blood, semen, vaginal secretions, or breast milk.**

Risky Behaviors There are four main ways that HIV spreads from person to person.

- **Sexual Contact** HIV can be transmitted through any form of sexual contact that involves contact with an infected person's body fluids, including vaginal, oral, and anal sex. Infected fluids can enter a person's bloodstream through sores or tiny cuts in the lining of the mouth, vagina, rectum, or opening of the penis.
- **Shared Needles** HIV can be transmitted through shared needles or syringes that are contaminated with the blood of an infected person. Therefore, sharing needles for tattoos or body piercings and injecting illegal drugs put you at risk for HIV infection.
- **Contact With Blood** HIV can be transmitted if a person has an open cut or sore that comes into contact with the blood or blood parts of an infected person. Avoid all contact with others' blood.
- **Mother to Baby** HIV can pass from an infected mother to her child, either during pregnancy, birth, or breast-feeding. Certain drugs can decrease the chances of transmission during pregnancy, and the doctor might deliver the baby by cesarean section to reduce the risk of transmission during birth. In addition, mothers infected with HIV should not breast-feed their babies.

GO ONLINE
PearsonSuccessNet.com
For: More on AIDS

FIGURE 10 It is safer for an HIV-positive mother to bottle-feed, rather than breast-feed, her baby.

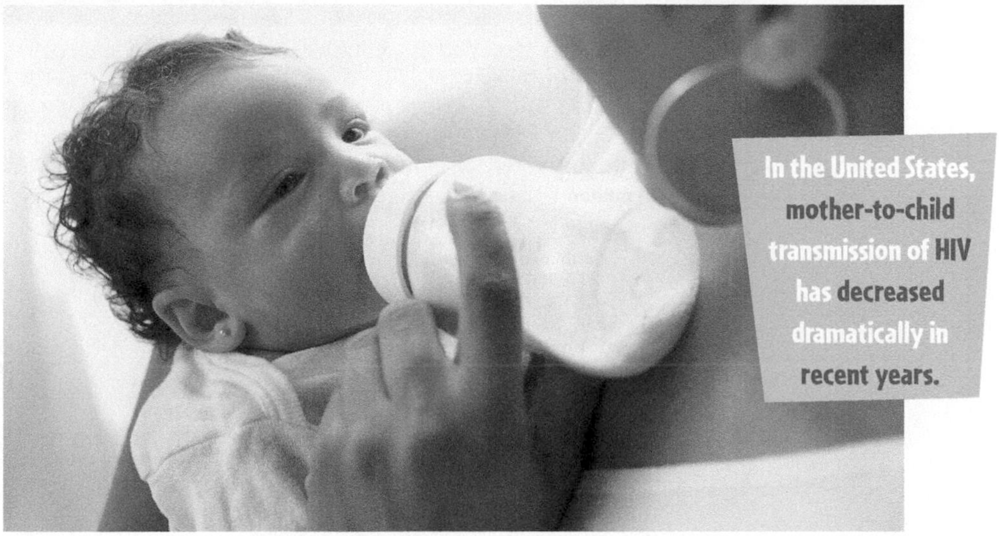

Transmission of HIV

L3 Content Update GO ONLINE

Visit Pearson SuccessNet to access more information about AIDS. Have students complete the Web activity.

L3 Building Health Skills

Practicing Healthful Behaviors Ask: **What risky behaviors increase the risk of HIV infection in teens and adults?** *(sexual contact, shared drug needles, contact with others' blood)* Have the class brainstorm healthful behaviors they could practice to decrease the risk of HIV infection. *(Sample answers: Practice sexual abstinence; do not use drugs.)* Encourage students to put the healthful behaviors into practice.

L2 Cooperative Learning

Divide students into groups and ask them to create a warning to other teens about the potential risk of HIV infection from tattoos and body piercings. They may create a poster or a presentation. Suggest that students include statistics on risks of infection and visuals explaining how contaminated needles can spread HIV from one person to another.

L2 Visual Learning: Figure 10

Have students read about mother-to-child transmission of HIV in the figure. Ask: **When can HIV pass from an infected mother to her child?** *(during pregnancy, birth, and breast-feeding)* **What practices can decrease the chances of HIV passing from an infected mother to her child during these three times?** *(taking certain drugs during pregnancy, delivering the baby by cesarean section, and bottle-feeding, respectively)*

Differentiated Instruction

L4 Gifted and Talented

Ask interested students to interview a local public health official about HIV and AIDS. Students might ask which modes of transmission are most common locally, how local cases of HIV infection and AIDS are reported, and what progress is being made in developing an HIV vaccine. Have students share what they learn in an oral report to the class.

L1 Building Health Skills

Communicating Some students may still have fears about being infected with HIV through casual contact. Ask students to write their fears on anonymous slips of paper and give them to you at the end of class. At the next class, write the different fears on the board. Then pair up students and have each member of a pair choose one of the fears listed on the board. Students should explain to each other (or write an explanation) in understandable terms why that fear is unfounded and reinforce the safe behaviors discussed in the text.

L3 Active Learning

Have interested students contact their local chapter of the American Red Cross and find out how potential donors are screened for HIV risk factors and how donated blood is tested for HIV infection. If possible, students should obtain a copy of the questionnaire that potential donors must fill out to be considered as donors. Ask students to create a bulletin board to display what they learn.

A Global Problem

L3 Visual Learning: Figure 12

Image Bank Figure 22-12

Caption Answer From greatest to smallest, the list is: Sub-Saharan Africa (23.5 million), South and Southeast Asia (4 million), Latin America (1.4 million), Eastern Europe and Central Asia (1.4 million), North America (1.4 million), Western Europe (900,000), East Asia (830,000), North Africa and Middle East (300,000), Caribbean (230,000), Oceania (53,000). North America, along with Latin America and Eastern Europe and Central Asia, has the third highest number of people living with HIV.

FIGURE 11 Playing contact sports such as rugby does not put you at risk for HIV infection.

Safe Behaviors HIV is not transmitted by casual contact. You cannot get HIV by going to classes or eating lunch with an infected person. You cannot get HIV by holding hands or hugging an infected person. Families who live with an infected person are not at risk of contracting HIV unless they engage in high-risk behaviors. Small amounts of HIV occur in saliva, tears, and perspiration. However, the amounts are so small that infection from contact with these fluids is unlikely.

The Safety of Donated Blood The risk of getting HIV from blood transfusions is extremely small. Since 1985, all of the blood collected in the United States has been tested for the presence of HIV. Blood that tests positive for HIV antibodies is discarded. Potential donors are interviewed and are not allowed to give blood if they have engaged in behaviors that place them at risk for HIV infection.

A Global Problem

Figure 12 shows the global distribution of HIV infections. **With approximately 34 million people infected around the world, HIV and AIDS represent a global health problem.**

- **Africa** Sub-Saharan Africa accounts for 69% of all global infections. Some estimates indicate that, if infections continue to rise at the current rate, 80 million Africans may die from AIDS by 2025.
- **Asia** HIV infections are also increasing in certain parts of Asia. For example, researchers estimate that about 2.5 million people are living with HIV and AIDS in India.

FIGURE 12 The global distribution of HIV infections is uneven. **Sequencing** List the areas of the world from greatest number of infected people to smallest number of infected people. What position does North America have on the list?

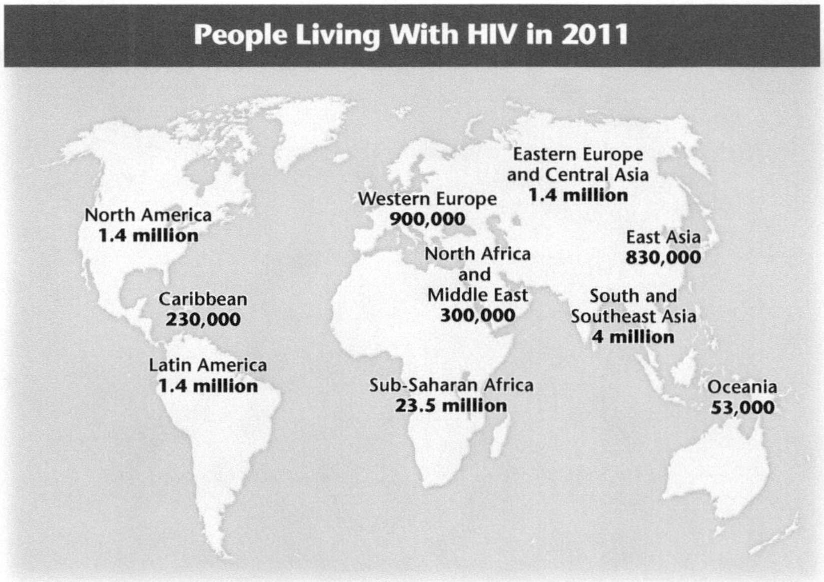

Focus on ISSUES

L3 Debate: AIDS Funding in Africa

Some people think the United States should contribute a significant amount to the billions of dollars a year needed to fight AIDS in Africa. Ask a few students to go online to learn more about the impact of AIDS in Africa, both on African nations and on the rest of the world. Then, have students choose sides and debate whether the United States should be expected to pay so much to help fight AIDS in Africa. After the debate, discuss why AIDS in Africa should concern people throughout the world.

High-Risk Groups In all areas of the world, HIV is spreading among people who share needles to inject drugs and people who engage in high-risk sexual behaviors. In many countries, young women represent the majority of new HIV infections. In sub-Saharan Africa, for example, 75% of young people infected with HIV are female. The higher infection rates in women are often due to a lack of information about how to protect themselves or, in some cases, a lack of power to protect themselves.

FIGURE 13 A girl from Zambia, a country in Africa, holds a sign she made for World AIDS Day.

Education and Prevention Several international organizations are working to lessen the toll that HIV and AIDS are taking on populations all over the world. The World Health Organization and the Joint United Nations Programme on HIV/AIDS monitor the situation and recommend steps for stemming the epidemic in different countries.

The main goal of international organizations is HIV education. Making people in high-risk countries aware of how to protect themselves from HIV infection is a huge step toward prevention. Because treatment can be very expensive and inaccessible for the people at highest risk, much effort is put toward preventing HIV infection in the first place.

In addition to prevention education, international organizations coordinate treatment efforts for people already living with HIV and AIDS. Efforts are being made to provide medicine to millions of infected people in countries most affected by HIV and AIDS.

Section 3 Review

Key Ideas and Vocabulary

1. Explain how HIV affects the immune system and how it eventually leads to AIDS.
2. What is meant by an **opportunistic infection**? Give an example.
3. What are four ways that HIV can be transmitted from an infected person to an uninfected person? List three ways HIV is *not* transmitted.
4. Which region of the world accounts for the majority of HIV infections?

Critical Thinking

5. **Making Judgments** Should teens in the United States be concerned about the global AIDS problem? Why or why not?

Health at School

AIDS Awareness Plan an AIDS Awareness Day at your school. Divide your class into groups to make posters about different aspects of HIV and AIDS. For example, one poster could focus on how HIV is transmitted. Another poster could focus on the status of the AIDS epidemic. Display your posters at school to help educate other students. **WRITING**

6. **Evaluating** HIV is more common in poorer countries than in wealthier countries. Why do you think this might be the case?

3. Assess

Evaluate

These assignments can help you assess students' mastery of the section content.

L3 Section 3 Review

Answers appear below.

L2 Reteach

Ask students to write a paragraph in which they correctly use each of the section vocabulary terms. Have pairs of students exchange and check for errors in one another's completed paragraphs. Partners should work together to rewrite any incorrect sentences.

L4 Enrich

Health at School

AIDS Awareness Divide the class into groups, and assign a different aspect of HIV/AIDS to each group. After groups complete their posters, arrange for students to hold poster sessions in the cafeteria during lunch periods on AIDS Awareness Day. At the sessions, students can use their posters to educate other students about AIDS.

Section 3 Review

1. HIV attacks specific cells of the immune system, disabling the body's defenses against other pathogens. When the immune system becomes severely disabled, the infected person has AIDS.
2. An opportunistic infection is an infection that attacks a person with a weakened immune system. Students may give any one of the following examples: tuberculosis, fungal infections, and pneumocystis carinii pneumonia.
3. HIV can be transmitted through sexual contact, shared needles, contact with blood, and from mother to baby. HIV is not transmitted through casual contact, such as going to classes, eating lunch, or holding hands with an infected person.
4. sub-Saharan Africa
5. Answers may vary, but they should be logical and show awareness of the dangers of a global HIV/AIDS problem.
6. *Sample answer:* because there is less money in poorer countries to educate people about how to prevent AIDS

Sexually Transmitted Infections and AIDS **103**

Section 4

Protecting Yourself From HIV and AIDS

Objectives
Before class begins, write the objectives on the board. Have students copy the objectives into their notebooks at the start of class.

1. Focus

Warm-Up Advice

After students finish writing, ask: **Why is abstinence the only sure way to avoid becoming infected with HIV and other STIs?** *(Accept all reasonable answers. Sample answers: You usually can't tell if your partner is infected. Condoms are not 100% effective against HIV and other STIs.)* Tell students they will learn additional ways to avoid HIV infection when they read this section.

Connect to Your Life It is much easier to avoid risky behaviors if you choose friends who have also decided to avoid risky behaviors.

Sensitive Issues

Students may worry that they are infected with HIV but be reluctant to get tested for fear other people will find out. Tell students there are confidential testing centers for HIV. Stress the importance of getting tested so treatment can begin as soon as possible. Explain that the sooner treatment begins, the more effective it is likely to be.

Section 4

Protecting Yourself From HIV and AIDS

Objectives

- **Identify** three behaviors that can prevent the spread of HIV.
- **Describe** how a person gets tested for HIV.
- **Describe** the goal of HIV treatment.

Vocabulary

- **universal precautions**
- **HIV-positive**
- **viral load**

Warm-Up

Dear Advice Line,

Lately my boyfriend has been asking me to have sex. I really like him, but I'm not ready for that. Plus I'm not sure he's telling me everything about his past. What should I do?

WRITING Write a response to this teen, encouraging her to choose abstinence. What would you tell her about the risk of becoming infected with HIV and other STIs?

Preventing HIV Infection

At present there is no cure for HIV or AIDS. But, the good news is that you can choose behaviors that will help you avoid this very serious disease. **You can protect yourself from HIV by practicing abstinence, avoiding drugs, and avoiding contact with others' blood and body fluids.**

Practice Abstinence As with other STIs, the best way to avoid HIV and AIDS is sexual abstinence. Sexual activity such as oral sex, anal sex, genital-to-genital touching, and intercourse can transmit HIV. It is much easier to be abstinent if you choose friends who have also decided to be abstinent. Going out with groups of responsible friends can reduce the pressure you may feel to engage in sexual behavior.

Avoid Drugs Avoiding drug use is also extremely important for reducing the risk of HIV infection. People who share contaminated needles to inject themselves with drugs are at a high risk for contracting HIV. People who have sex with drug abusers are also at high risk. Do not inject illegal drugs, and avoid sexual contact with anyone who uses illegal drugs.

Using alcohol or other drugs can impair a person's judgment. People with impaired judgment are more likely to engage in behaviors that place them at risk. To guard against infection, you need to be able to think clearly so you can make healthy decisions.

Connect to Your Life **How can your choice of friends help you avoid risky behaviors?**

TEENS *Are Asking . . .*

Q: I heard that heterosexual people hardly ever get HIV infections or AIDS as long as they don't get involved in drugs. Is that a myth or a fact?

A: It's a myth, and a very dangerous one! In 2003, almost one third of new cases of AIDS in adolescents and adults were transmitted through heterosexual contact. All sexually active people are at risk of HIV infection, unless they are absolutely certain their partners are free of HIV. Otherwise, virtually any type of sexual contact can present a risk for transmission of HIV.

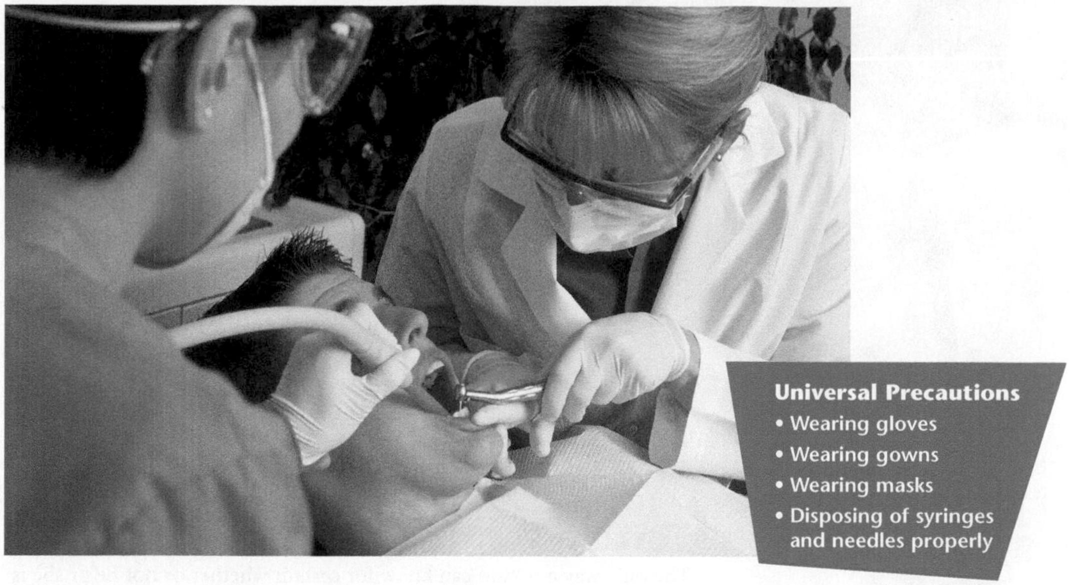

FIGURE 14 Healthcare providers protect themselves and their patients by following universal precautions.

Avoid Contact With Blood or Body Fluids Never share any personal items that may have blood or other body fluids on them. For example, razors, toothbrushes, syringes, and piercing or tattoo needles should never be shared. In addition, mothers who are infected with HIV should not breast-feed their babies because the virus can be transmitted through breast milk.

Healthcare providers often come into contact with the blood and body fluids of patients. To reduce the risk of HIV transmission, doctors, nurses, dentists, dental hygienists, and other healthcare providers practice **universal precautions,** as listed in Figure 14.

Sexual Fidelity If two people are uninfected with HIV at the start of a monogamous relationship such as marriage, sexual fidelity by both partners will protect them from HIV. However, if either partner has practiced risky behaviors in the past, he or she should be tested for HIV and other STIs. Teens should *not* count on sexual fidelity to protect them from HIV.

Barrier Protection For people who are sexually active, but not in a monogamous relationship, the best way to reduce their risk of HIV infection is to use a condom every time they engage in sexual activity. The condom must be made out of latex or polyurethane, be free of tears, and be used in accordance with the directions on the package. Condoms serve as a physical barrier against HIV and some of the pathogens that cause STIs. When used consistently and correctly, condoms are highly effective in preventing the spread of HIV. However, condoms are not 100% effective. Abstinence remains the best protection against HIV and other STIs.

2. Teach

Preventing HIV Infection

L2 Building Health Skills

Advocacy Have groups of students make posters advocating healthful behaviors that help prevent HIV infection. Posters should cover practicing abstinence, avoiding drugs, and the other behaviors described in the text. Posters should also be factually correct, attention-getting, and relevant to teens. Ask students to arrange to display their posters in places on and off campus where many teens will see them, such as the school cafeteria and local YMCA lobby.

L3 Journal Writing

Ask students to write a private journal entry describing ways they could respond to someone who pressures them to engage in sexual activity. Their responses should include reasons relating to HIV and other STIs. Encourage students to put their ideas into practice if they ever find themselves in such a situation. **WRITING**

L4 Active Learning

Have interested students interview dental hygienists or dental assistants about precautions they take to prevent contact with HIV and other infections. Ask the students to share what they learn with the class. Discuss how their reports relate to the universal precautions listed in Figure 14.

Differentiated Instruction

L2 Less Proficient Readers

As students read, tell them to look for information related to the section objectives that they copied into their notebooks earlier. Below or beside each objective, they should list relevant information. For example, for the first objective, they should list three behaviors that can prevent the spread of HIV. For the second objective, they should describe how a person gets tested for HIV. This exercise will help students focus on the most important points in the section.

Chapter 5, Section 4

Testing for HIV

L2 Addressing Misconceptions

HIV Testing Students may assume that HIV testing involves looking for the virus in blood. Tell them that HIV testing involves looking for antibodies to HIV in blood, not the virus itself, and it takes weeks or even months before there are enough antibodies to be detected. Explain that antibodies are proteins produced by an infected person's immune system in an (unsuccessful) attempt to fight the virus. People with antibodies to HIV in their blood are infected with HIV.

L3 Cultural Connection

Tell students that cultural beliefs make some people reluctant to be tested for HIV. For example, many Vietnamese and other Southeast Asian immigrants in the United States think that it is dangerous to have their blood drawn for testing, including HIV testing. This is because they believe that taking blood weakens the body. Ask students whether they know of similar beliefs in other cultures. Discuss how reluctance to be tested can adversely affect the health of people with HIV by delaying diagnosis and treatment.

L3 Class Discussion

Explain that most HIV testing centers provide counseling to people who test positive for HIV. Ask: **Why do you think it is important for people who test positive for HIV to receive counseling?** *(Sample answers: so they can learn how to avoid passing the virus to others; so they can get help coping with an incurable infection)*

Connect to Your Life *Sample answer:* by explaining that it could take months for antibodies to HIV to show up in the person's blood

FIGURE 15 A blood test can reveal if a person is infected with HIV. Getting an HIV-positive result can be frightening and depressing. Therefore, it is important that HIV-positive individuals receive counseling to help them deal with the emotional impacts of their infection.

Testing for HIV

The only way a person can know for certain whether or not he or she is infected with HIV is to have a blood test. People who engage in risky behaviors should have their blood tested at a clinic or by a private physician. The names of clinics that provide confidential HIV testing are available from each state's department of public health or from the Centers for Disease Control and Prevention. People who think they may have been exposed to HIV should practice abstinence to avoid spreading the virus.

In an HIV test, a person's blood is tested for antibodies to HIV. If antibodies are detected, a second test is done to verify the result. A person who is diagnosed as being infected with HIV is said to be **HIV-positive.**

An HIV-Positive Diagnosis If a person is diagnosed as HIV-positive, he or she needs to notify all previous sexual partners so that they can also be tested. Early diagnosis is important to prevent the spread of the disease and to start treatment as soon as possible.

It is difficult to cope with an HIV-positive diagnosis. For this reason, it is recommended that individuals receive counseling from a healthcare professional before being tested. People who learn they are HIV-positive should receive additional counseling.

Reasons for Follow-Up Testing If an HIV infection is recent, a blood test may not be accurate. This is because there is a lapse between the time of infection and the time when antibodies show up in a person's blood. Antibodies usually show up within three months after infection. So even if no antibodies are detected in the person's first blood test, he or she should avoid all high-risk behaviors and be tested again in three months.

Connect to Your Life **How could you convince someone of the importance of follow-up testing?**

MATH and Health

L3 Estimating

Remind students that 1.2 million people in the United States had HIV infections in 2008. Point out in Figure 16 that the medical costs for a person with HIV may be at least \$25,000 per year. Ask students to use these data to estimate the total medical costs of HIV infections in the United States in 2008. (about \$25,000 per person × 1.2 million people = at least \$30 billion total cost) Discuss why the answer is just an estimate and why it may be an underestimate.

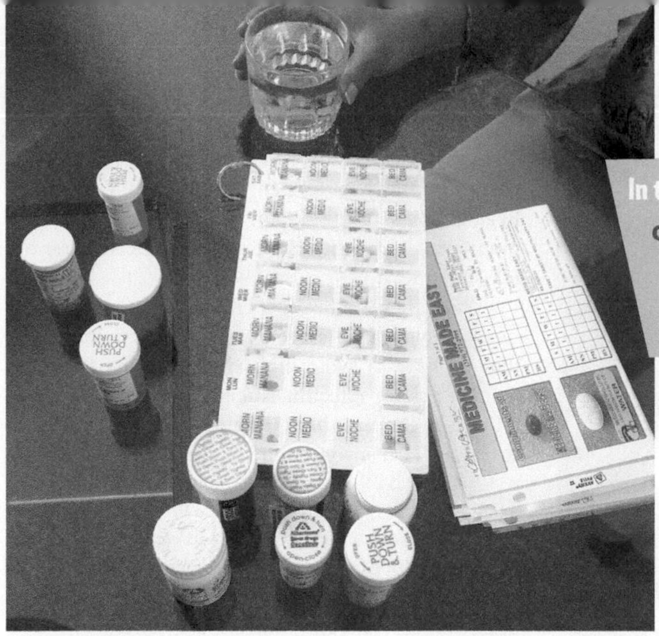

In the United States, medical costs for a person living with HIV are about $25,000 a year.

FIGURE 16 A common treatment regimen requires an HIV-positive person to take many pills each day. If the person misses too many doses, the virus may develop resistance to the medication.

Treatment for HIV and AIDS

Although there is no cure for HIV infection and AIDS, some treatments can add many years to a patient's life. The sooner a person begins treatment, the more effective it can be in slowing the progress of the disease.

The Goal of Treatment **The main goal of HIV treatment is to keep the person's immune system functioning as close to normal as possible.** To achieve this goal, the treatment must

- keep the person's **viral load**—the number of virus particles circulating in the body—as low as possible, and
- keep the person's T cell count as high as possible.

If both of these goals are achieved, the patient's immune system is more capable of fighting off opportunistic infections. Remember that current treatments do not rid the body of HIV. They try to stop HIV from destroying the immune system.

Combination Drug Therapy The most common treatment for HIV infection today is known as Highly Active AntiRetroviral Therapy, or HAART. HAART uses a combination of drugs to reduce the viral load in the blood. Multiple drugs are necessary to prevent the virus from reproducing inside helper T cells. A doctor prescribes a combination of drugs that is right for each individual patient.

Some drawbacks to HAART are its complicated dosage schedules, its cost, and its side effects, which can include liver and kidney damage. Furthermore, if a person is not consistent about taking the drugs exactly as prescribed, drug resistance can develop quickly.

GO ONLINE
PearsonSuccessNet.com
For: More on HIV/AIDS prevention

Treatment for HIV and AIDS

EL Cooperative Learning

Explain that a major problem in treatment of HIV and AIDS is compliance, or getting people to take all of their medicine correctly and to keep taking it for life. Sometimes, language can be an obstacle in getting people to comply with their treatment regimen. Challenge small groups of students to brainstorm ways to help people with HIV and AIDS—both English speakers and non-English speakers—comply with treatment. Encourage the English language learners in each group to come up with ideas for making treatment more understandable for people who speak their native language. *(Ways might include calendars or other reminder systems for taking medications, patient education pamphlets, or programs conveying the dangers of discontinuing treatment.)*

L2 Building Health Skills

Practicing Healthful Behaviors
Volunteering to help others is good for one's emotional health. Have students find out how they can volunteer to help people in their community who are living with HIV. Suggest that they get ideas from local professionals (e.g., nurses, doctors, social workers) who serve HIV-positive people. (Possible ideas might include doing yard work or other chores for people with HIV.) Urge students to follow through with their ideas and, in doing so, practice behaviors that promote their own emotional health.

L3 Online Activity GO ONLINE

Visit Pearson SuccessNet to access an online activity about HIV/AIDS prevention. Have students complete the Web activity.

Differentiated Instruction

L1 Special Needs

Ask volunteers to help you demonstrate ways that HIV is *not* spread, such as shaking hands with, sitting close to, or using the same book as someone with HIV. Explain that this is why it is safe to go to school with people with HIV. Encourage students to be supportive of any people they know who are HIV-positive.

3. Assess

Evaluate
These assignments can help you assess students' mastery of the section content.

L3 Section 4 Review
Answers appear below.

L2 Reteach
Ask students to rewrite the section objectives as questions and then write answers to the questions. They can check their answers by rereading relevant passages in the text.

L4 Enrich

Health at School

HIV Prevention You may want to speak with teachers in grades six to eight about the program before students contact them. Check that students' outlines are accurate and complete. Ask students how they will convey the information covered in their outlines. Remind them that the material should be presented in ways that are suitable for younger students. Urge students to develop their programs and arrange to present them to classes in lower grades. You can ask the teachers of the classes to give you feedback on students' presentations.

FIGURE 17 Every year, thousands of people participate in walks to help raise money for AIDS research and education.

Living With HIV People who are HIV-positive must take extra care to practice healthful behaviors. Eating right, exercising, and getting plenty of sleep are especially important for people who are HIV-positive. Regular visits to the doctor are also important for monitoring a patient's health and the effectiveness of HIV treatment.

When they are healthy, HIV-positive people can carry on with their careers and other activities. But they do have to avoid high-risk behaviors that put them at risk for infecting someone else. And because HIV compromises the immune system, they should stay away from anyone who has an infectious disease.

The Need for Support As with any serious disease, people who are HIV-positive as well as their loved ones need a lot of support to help them deal with their distress and anxiety. Support may include counseling, healthcare services, and financial assistance.

HIV-positive individuals should be treated with compassion. They also should be allowed to live their lives with dignity. Because HIV cannot be transmitted by casual contact, such as hugging or shaking hands, no one needs to be fearful of working or going to school with someone who is HIV-positive.

Section 4 Review

Key Ideas and Vocabulary

1. What are three behaviors that can help you avoid HIV infection?
2. What does an HIV test involve?
3. What does **HIV-positive** mean?
4. What is the main goal of HIV treatment? How is that goal achieved?

Critical Thinking

5. **Evaluating** Depression can be a serious problem in people who are HIV-positive. What do you think are some ways to help people deal with the mental and emotional effects of this disease?

Health at School

HIV Prevention Some schools introduce HIV prevention education in grades six to eight. Find out if you or a group of classmates could prepare a program to help educate these younger students about protecting themselves from HIV infection. Then, develop an outline for your program. **WRITING**

6. **Relating Cause and Effect** Doctors recommend that people who are HIV-positive should stay as healthy as possible, eating well, getting enough sleep, and avoiding exposure to anyone with an infectious disease. Why do doctors recommend this?

Section 4 Review

1. *Any three:* practice abstinence, avoid drugs, avoid contact with others' blood or body fluids, practice sexual fidelity in marriage, use barrier protection
2. It involves testing a person's blood for antibodies to HIV and retesting to verify the result if antibodies are detected.
3. It means a person is infected with HIV.
4. The main goal is to keep the person's immune system functioning as close to normal as possible. That goal is achieved by using a combination of drugs to reduce the viral load in the blood and prevent the virus from reproducing inside helper T cells.
5. *Sample answer:* reach out to loved ones for support, see a mental health professional
6. People who are HIV-positive have compromised immune systems. Healthy behaviors help to strengthen their immune systems and reduce their exposure to infections.

Chapter 5 Review

VIDEO **TEENS Talk**

Risks and STIs List three things you learned from the video about the importance of sexual abstinence.

Reviewing Key Ideas

Section 1

1. Being unable to have children is
   a. STI. b. epidemic.
   c. infertility. d. abstinence.
2. How can teens best avoid STIs?
3. List four kinds of sexual activity that can transmit STIs.
4. **Critical Thinking** If you found out that the person you were dating had injected illegal drugs in the past, how would that affect your relationship?

Section 2

5. A serious infection of the female reproductive organs that can be caused by chlamydia is
   a. pelvic inflammatory disease.
   b. genital warts.
   c. syphilis.
   d. trichomoniasis.
6. An STI that *cannot* be treated with antibiotics is
   a. gonorrhea. b. chlamydia.
   c. human papilloma virus. d. syphilis.
7. How can genital herpes affect a newborn baby?
8. What steps should be taken by a person who suspects that he or she is infected with an STI?
9. **Critical Thinking** Why should someone who is diagnosed with an STI notify all of his or her sexual partners?

Section 3

10. The virus that causes AIDS is
    a. herpes. b. HPV.
    c. PID. d. HIV.
11. HIV destroys
    a. neurons. b. antibodies.
    c. B cells. d. T cells.
12. Why do people with AIDS fall victim to opportunistic infections?
13. Describe four ways that HIV is spread.
14. **Critical Thinking** Jason has engaged in high-risk sexual behavior, but he feels fine. He sees no reason to get tested for HIV or any other STI. What would you tell Jason about the importance of getting tested?

Section 4

15. Which of these behaviors is *not* a way to protect yourself from HIV?
    a. avoiding contact with blood
    b. practicing abstinence
    c. sharing needles
    d. avoiding alcohol
16. HIV-positive people receive treatments to keep
    a. their viral load as high as possible.
    b. their viral load as low as possible.
    c. their viral load equal to their T cell count.
    d. their T cell count as low as possible.
17. In what ways can HIV treatment be difficult?
18. **Critical Thinking** Alyssa has engaged in high-risk sexual behavior in the past three months. She had an HIV test a month ago that came back negative. Should she be tested again? Explain.
19. **Critical Thinking** Experts consider education critical in preventing HIV infection. Do you agree? Explain your answer.

Building Health Skills

20. **Analyzing Influences** Do the media do a good job in educating people about HIV and other STIs? Give examples to support your answer.
21. **Advocacy** What could teens do to make abstinence an easier choice for their peers?
22. **Setting Goals** List some goals you have for the next ten years. How could practicing abstinence now help you achieve those goals? **WRITING**

Health and Community

Public Service Announcement Some people behave in sexually risky ways. In many cases, they don't get tested regularly for HIV or other STIs. Create a public service announcement that emphasizes the risks of certain behaviors and the importance of getting tested. Indicate where people in your community can go to get tested for HIV and other STIs. **WRITING**

Chapter 5 Review

Reviewing Key Ideas

Section 1

1. c
2. Teens can best avoid STIs by practicing sexual abstinence.
3. oral sex, anal sex, genital-to-genital touching, and intercourse
4. Answers will vary but should reveal knowledge that STIs can be spread by injecting illegal drugs.

Section 2

5. a
6. c
7. It can cause blindness and death.
8. The person should refrain from sexual activity and see a doctor immediately.
9. so they can refrain from sexual activity and seek treatment

Section 3

10. d
11. d
12. because their immune system is weakened by HIV
13. through sexual contact, via shared needles, through direct contact with infected blood, and from an infected mother to her baby
14. Answers should reveal knowledge that STIs do not always cause symptoms and that treatment is important.

Section 4

15. c
16. b
17. Drug dosage schedules are complicated, the drugs are costly, and they can have serious side effects.
18. Yes, because it may take at least three months for HIV antibodies to show up in her blood.
19. Answers should show that students realize people need to know the risks in order to prevent HIV infection.

Building Health Skills

20. Answers may vary. Some students might say that the media do not do a good job and cite examples from television or movies of people engaging in sexual contact, apparently without risk of STIs. Other students might say that the media do a good job and cite examples of public service announcements warning people about HIV and other STIs.
21. *Sample answers:* Support peers' decisions to avoid risky behaviors. Set a good example for peers by avoiding risky behaviors themselves.
22. *Sample answer:* My goals are going to college and becoming a teacher. Practicing abstinence could help me achieve my goals by helping to keep me healthy and by preventing me from getting pregnant.

Health and Community

Public Service Announcement Suggest that students contact their state public health department or the CDC to find out where people in their community can get tested for STIs. Students' announcements should explain the role of testing in curbing transmission and getting appropriate treatment.

Glossary

A

abstinence The act of refraining from, or not having, sex. (p. 46)
abstinencia Acción de privarse de tener relaciones sexuales.

adolescence The period from about age 12 to 19 during which a child gradually changes into an adult. (p. 9)
adolescencia Período entre los 12 y los 19 años aproximadamente, durante el cual un(a) niño(a) se convierte gradualmente en adulto.

AIDS Acquired immunodeficiency syndrome, an often fatal disease of the immune system caused by HIV infection. (p. 98)
SIDA Sigla del síndrome de inmunodeficiencia adquirida, una enfermedad del sistema inmunológico, por lo general fatal, causada por el virus de inmunodeficiencia humana (VIH).

amniocentesis A prenatal test in which a small amount of amniotic fluid is removed and tested for abnormalities. (p. 71)
amniocentesis Examen prenatal que consiste en extraer una pequeña cantidad de líquido amniótico y someterlo a pruebas para detectar anormalidades.

amniotic sac A fluid-filled bag of thin tissue that develops around the embryo. (p. 66)
saco amniótico Bolsa de tejido fino, llena de líquido, que se forma alrededor del feto.

asymptomatic stage The stage of HIV infection in which the infected person shows no symptoms. (p. 99)
etapa asintomática Etapa de la infección del VIH durante la cual la persona infectada no muestra síntomas.

B

bisexual A person who is sexually attracted to people of both sexes. (p. 13)
bisexual Persona que siente atracción sexual por gente de ambos sexos.

blastocyst A hollow, spherical structure made up of about 50 to 100 cells that attaches to the uterus during implantation. (p. 65)
blastocisto Estructura hueca de forma esférica, con aproximadamente 50 to 100 células, que se adhiere al útero durante la implatación.

body image The way a person sees his or her physical self. (p. 12)
imagen corporal La manera en que una persona se ve a sí misma físicamente.

C

chancre A painless sore that appears during the first stage of syphilis infection. (p. 96)
chancro Llaga indolora que aparece en la primera etapa de la sífilis.

chlamydia A very common sexually transmitted infection caused by bacteria. (p. 93)
linfogranuloma venéreo Infección de transmisión sexual muy común, causada por una bacteria.

chorionic villus sampling A prenatal test in which a piece of the developing placenta is removed and tested for inherited disorders. (p. 71)
muestra de vellosidad coriónica Prueba prenatal que consiste en sacar un fragmento de la placenta y examinarlo para detectar trastornos hereditarios.

commitment A strong determination to make a marriage a fulfilling, lifelong relationship. (p. 61)
compromiso Fuerte determinación para hacer de un matrimonio una relación satisfactoria y de por vida.

compatibility The ability of particular people to live together in harmony. (p. 61)
compatibilidad Capacidad de cierta gente para vivir junta y en armonía.

compromise An agreement in which each party gives up something. (p. 61)
concesión Acuerdo por el cual cada participante cede algo.

contraception or birth control The use of any accepted method to intentionally prevent pregnancy. (p. 77)
contracepción o control de la natalidad Uso de cualquier métado aceptado para prevenir el embarazo.

cystitis An infection of the urinary bladder. (p. 34)
cistitis Infección de la vejiga urinaria.

D

date rape A rape that occurs during a date. (p. 51)
violación en una cita Violación que ocurre en el transcurso de una cita.

dating violence A pattern of physical, emotional, or sexual abuse that occurs in a dating relationship. (p. 49)
violencia en el noviazgo Patrón de maltrato físico, emocional, o sexual que se presenta entre dos personas que son novios.

E

ectopic pregnancy A condition resulting from the implantation of the blastocyst in a location in the abdomen other than the uterus. (p. 72)
embarazo ectópico Condición causada por la implantación del blastocisto en una zona del abdomen que no sea el útero.

effectiveness In reference to a contraceptive method, the likelihood that using that method will prevent pregnancy. (p. 77)
efectividad En referencia a un método contraceptivo, la posibilidad de que el uso de un método prevenga el embarazo.

ejaculation The ejection of semen from the penis. (p. 22)
eyaculación Eyección del semen por el pene.

embryo The stage of human development from the two-cell stage until about nine weeks after fertilization. (p. 65)
embrión Etapa del desarrollo humano que tiene lugar a partir de la división del cigoto en dos células hasta aproximadamente la novena semana después de la fecundación.

emotional abuse The nonphysical mistreatment of a person. (p. 49)
maltrato emocional Todo maltrato que no sea de índole físico.

emotional intimacy The openness, sharing, affection, and trust that can develop in a close relationship. (p. 46)
intimidad emocional Franqueza, comunicación intensa, afecto y confianza que se desarrollan en una relación íntima.

erection The state in which the penis becomes larger and stiffer as chambers in it become filled with blood. (p. 22)
erección Estado en el que el pene crece y se endurece a medida que los cuerpos cavernosos del pene se llenan de sangre.

estrogen The female sex hormone that signals certain physical changes at puberty and controls the maturation of eggs. (p. 27)
estrógeno Hormona sexual femenina que regula ciertos cambios físicos durante la pubertad, así como la maduración de los óvulos.

F

failure rate In reference to a contraceptive method, the percentage of women who become pregnant while using that method for one year. (p. 77)
tasa de fracasos En referencia a un método contraceptivo, el porcentaje de mujeres que quedan embarazadas mientras usan ese método específico durante un año.

fallopian tubes The passageways that carry eggs from the ovaries to the uterus. (p. 28)
trompas de Falopio Tubos que transportan los óvulos desde los ovarios al útero.

fertilization The process of a sperm cell joining with an egg. (p. 20)
fecundación Proceso mediante el cual un espermatozoide se une con un óvulo.

fetus The stage of human development from the third month after fertilization until birth. (p. 67)
feto Etapa del desarrollo humano que tiene lugar a partir del tercer mes después de la fecundación hasta el nacimiento.

G

gender The way people perceive maleness or femaleness to be defined by society. (p. 4)
género La manera en que la gente percibe la masculinidad o femineidad para ser definidos por la sociedad.

gender roles The behaviors and attitudes that are socially accepted as either masculine or feminine. (p. 5)
papeles sexuales Conductas y actitudes que son socialmente aceptadas como masculinas o femeninas.

genital herpes A sexually transmitted infection caused by the herpes simplex virus. (p. 95)
herpes genital Infección de transmisión sexual causada por el virus del herpes simple.

gestational diabetes Diabetes that develops during pregnancy. (p. 72)
diabetes gestacional Diabetes que se desarrolla durante el embarazo.

gonorrhea A bacterial sexually transmitted infection that infects the urinary tract of males and females and the reproductive organs of females. (p. 94)
gonorrea Infección bacterial de transmisión sexual que infecta las vías urinarias del hombre y los órganos reproductores de la mujer.

H

heterosexual A person who is sexually attracted to members of the opposite sex. (p. 13)
heterosexual Persona que se siente atraída sexualmente por personas del sexo opuesto.

HIV The human immunodeficiency virus, an incurable sexually transmitted infection that can lead to AIDS. (p. 98)
VIH Virus de inmunodeficiencia humana, una infección de transmisión sexual incurable que puede producir el SIDA.

HIV-positive A person who is diagnosed as being infected with HIV. (p. 106)
VIH-positivo Persona que se diagnostica como infectada con el VIH.

homosexual A person who is sexually attracted to members of the same sex. (p. 13)
homosexual Persona que se siente atraída sexualmente por personas del mismo sexo.

human papilloma virus A very common viral sexually transmitted infection. (p. 93)
virus del papiloma humano Infección viral de transmisión sexual muy común.

hymen A thin membrane that may partly cover the vaginal opening. (p. 29)
himen Delgada membrana que cubre parcialmente la abertura vaginal.

I

implantation The process in which the blastocyst attaches itself to the wall of the uterus. (p. 65)
implantación Proceso mediante el cual el blastocisto se adhiere a la pared del útero.

incest Sex between people who are too closely related to marry legally. (p. 52)
incesto Relación sexual entre personas de parentesco demasiado cercano como para poder casarse legalmente.

infatuation Feelings of intense attraction to another person. (p. 40)
enamoramiento Sentimiento de atracción intensa hacia otra persona.

infertility The condition of being unable to reproduce. (p. 26)
infertilidad Incapacidad para reproducirse.

M

mammogram An X-ray of the breast that may detect breast cancer. (p. 36)
mamografía Radiografía de la mama que permite detectar el cáncer de mama.

masturbation The touching of one's own genitals for sexual pleasure. (p. 23)
masturbación Tocarse los genitales propios para obtener placer sexual.

menopause The time of life during which the ovaries slow down their hormone production and no longer release mature eggs. (p. 31)
menopausia Período de la vida en el que los ovarios disminuyen su producción de hormonas y dejan de liberar óvulos maduros.

menstrual cycle The process during which an ovary releases a mature egg that travels to the uterus; if the egg is not fertilized, the uterine lining is shed and a new cycle begins. (p. 31)
ciclo menstrual Proceso mediante el cual el ovario libera un óvulo maduro que se dirige hacia el útero; si el óvulo no es fecundado, la capa uterina interna es expulsada y comienza un nuevo ciclo.

miscarriage The death of an embryo or fetus in the first 20 weeks of pregnancy. (p. 72)
aborto espontáneo Muerte de un embrión o feto en las primeras 20 semanas del embarazo.

monogamy A term describing a sexual relationship in which two people have sexual contact only with each other; also called sexual fidelity. (p. 91)
monogamia Término que describe una relación sexual en la cual dos personas tienen contacto sexual sólo entre ellas; también llamada fidelidad sexual.

N

nocturnal emission An ejaculation during sleep. Also called a "wet dream." (p. 23)
emisión nocturna Eyaculación durante el sueño. También llamado "sueño húmedo".

O

obstetrician A doctor who specializes in pregnancy and childbirth. (p. 70)
obstetra Médico que se especializa en el embarazo y el parto.

opportunistic infection An infection that attacks a person with a weakened immune system. (p. 100)
infección oportunista Infección que ataca a una persona que tiene debilitado el sistema inmunológico.

orgasm Sexual climax, marked by ejaculation in males and rhythmic contractions of the muscles of the vagina and pelvis in females. (p. 22)
orgasmo Clímax sexual, marcado por la eyaculación en los hombres y contracciones rítmicas de los músculos de la vagina y la pelvis en las mujeres.

ova The reproductive cells in females. (p. 27)
óvulos Células reproductoras femeninas.

ovaries The female reproductive glands. (p. 27)
ovarios Glándulas reproductoras femeninas.

ovulation The process during which one of the ovaries releases a ripened egg. (p. 27)
ovulación Proceso durante el cual un ovario libera un óvulo maduro.

P

Pap smear A medical procedure in which a sample of cells is taken from the cervix and examined under a microscope. (p. 36)
Prueba de Papanicolaou Procedimiento médico en que se toma una muestra de células del cuello uterino y se examinan bajo microscopio.

pedophilia A mental disorder in which a person has a sexual attraction to children. (p. 52)
pedofilia Trastorno mental en el que una persona siente atracción sexual por los niños.

pelvic inflammatory disease A serious infection of the female reproductive organs that can lead to infertility or an ectopic pregnancy. (p. 93)
enfermedad inflamatoria pélvica Infección grave de los órganos reproductores femeninos, que puede conducir a la infertilidad o al embarazo ectópico.

penis The external male sexual organ through which sperm leave the body. (p. 21)
pene Órgano sexual externo masculino a través del cual el cuerpo libera semen.

physical abuse Intentionally causing physical harm to another person. (p. 49)
maltrato físico Daño físico que se causa a otra persona de manera intencional.

placenta A structure that lines the wall of the uterus during pregnancy and nourishes the embryo or fetus with substances from the mother's blood. (p. 66)
placenta Estructura que recubre las paredas de útero durante el embarazo y alimenta al embrión o feto con sustancias de la sangre de la madre..

pornography Images and words that are designed to excite sexual arousal. (p. 56)
pornografía Imágenes y palabras destinadas a provocar excitación sexual.

preeclampsia A serious condition during pregnancy characterized by high blood pressure, swelling of the wrists and ankles, and high levels of protein in the urine. (p. 72)
preclampsia Trastorno serio del embarazo que se caracteriza por hipertensión arterial, inflamación de las muñecas y los tobillos, y la presencia de niveles elevados de proteínas en la orina.

prenatal care Medical care received during pregnancy. (p. 70)
cuidados prenatales Atención médica recibida durante el embarazo.

progesterone A hormone that signals changes to a woman's reproductive system during the menstrual cycle and pregnancy. (p. 27)
progesterona Hormona que regula los cambios del sistema reproductor de la mujer durante el ciclo menstrual y el embarazo.

prostitution When one person pays to have sex with another person. (p. 56)
prostitución Cuando una persona paga por tener relaciones sexuales con otra persona.

puberty The period of sexual development during which a person becomes sexually mature and physically able to reproduce. (p. 9)
pubertad Período de desarrollo sexual durante el cual la persona madura sexualmente y es capaz de reproducirse.

R

rape A type of assault in which one person forces another to have sexual relations. (p. 51)
violación Tipo de asalto en el cual una persona fuerza a otra a tener relaciones sexuales.

reproductive maturity The ability to produce children, signaled by the onset of ovulation in girls, and of sperm production in boys. (p. 10)
madurez reproductiva Capacidad de procrear, indicada por el comienzo de la ovulación en las niñas y la producción de espermatozoides en los niños.

S

scrotum A sac of skin that contains the testes. (p. 20)
escroto Bolsa de piel que contiene los testículos.

secondary sex characteristics Physical changes during puberty that are not directly involved in reproduction. (p. 10)
caracteres sexuales secundarios Cambios físicos que ocurren durante la pubertad y que no están directamente relacionados con la reproducción.

self-concept What a person thinks of himself or herself, physically and mentally. (p. 12)
autoconciencia Lo que una persona piensa de sí misma, tanto física como mentalmente.

semen The mixture of sperm and fluids produced by the glands of the male reproductive system. (p. 22)
semen Mezcla de espermatozoides y fluidos producidos por las glándulas del sistema reproductor masculino.

sexual abuse Forcing a person to engage in any unwanted sexual behavior. Includes rape and any use of a child by an adult for sexual purposes. (p. 49)
abuso sexual Forzar a una persona a mantener cualquier comportamiento sexual no deseado. Incluye violación y cualquier tipo de uso de un niño por parte de un adulto con propósitos sexuales.

sexual awakening The increased awareness of and sexual attraction to other people that begins around the time of puberty. (p. 13)
despertar sexual Aumento de la conciencia y de la atracción sexual hacia otras personas, que comienza alrededor de la época de la pubertad.

sexual harassment Any uninvited and unwelcome sexual remark or sexual advance. (p. 53)
acoso sexual Todo comentario o acción de carácter sexual que es mal recibido por una persona.

sexuality Everything that relates to, reflects, or expresses a person's maleness or femaleness. (p. 4)
sexualidad Todo lo relacionado, que refleja o expresa la femineidad o masculinidad de una persona.

sexually transmitted infection (STI) An infection caused by any pathogen that spreads from one person to another during sexual contact. (p. 88)
infección de transmisión sexual (ITS) Infección causada por cualquier patógeno que se transmite de una persona a otra por contacto sexual.

sperm The reproductive cells in males. (p. 20)
espermatozoides Células reproductoras masculinas.

spermicide A chemical agent that kills sperm. (p. 78)
espermicida Agente químico que mata los espermatozoides.

statutory rape Having sex with someone who is under the age of consent. (p. 51)
estupro Tener relaciones sexuales con una persona menor de la edad de consentimiento para tener relaciones sexuales.

sterilization The use of surgery or other procedure to make a person incapable of reproduction. (p. 81)
esterilización Uso de cirugía u otro procedimiento para hacer a una persona incapaz de reproducirse.

syphilis A serious bacterial sexually transmitted infection that progresses through three distinct stages. (p. 96)
sífilis Enfermedad bacterial grave de transmisión sexual que se desarrolla en tres etapas distintas.

T

testes The male reproductive glands. (p. 20)
testículos Glándulas reproductoras masculinas.

testicular torsion The twisting of a testis so that the blood vessels leading to the testis also twist, cutting off the blood supply. Testicular torsion is an emergency that requires immediate medical attention. (p. 24)
torsión testicular Retorcimiento de un testículo de modo que los vasos sanguíneos que llevan sangre al testículo también se retuercen, cortándose el flujo sanguíneo. La torsión testicular es una emergencia que requiere atención médica inmediata.

testosterone The sex hormone that affects the production of sperm and signals certain physical changes at puberty. (p. 20)
testosterona Hormona sexual que determina la producción de espermatozoides y regula ciertos cambios físicos durante la pubertad.

trichomoniasis A sexually transmitted infection caused by a protozoan that infects the urinary tract or vagina. (p. 92)
tricomoniasis Infección de transmisión sexual causada por un protozoo que infecta las vías urinarias o la vagina.

trimester One of three periods of time that divide a pregnancy. Each trimester is approximately three months long. (p. 70)
trimestre Cada uno de los tres períodos en los que se divide el embarazo. Cada trimestre dura aproximadamente tres meses.

U

ultrasound High-frequency sound waves used to create an image of a developing fetus. (p. 71)
ultrasonido Ondas sonoras de alta frecuencia utilizadas para crear una imagen del feto en desarrollo.

umbilical cord The cordlike structure that connects the embryo or fetus and the placenta. (p. 67)
cordón umbilical Estructura en forma de cuerda que conecta al embrión o feto con la placenta.

universal precautions Actions taken by healthcare providers that reduce their risk of coming into contact with blood and body fluids. (p. 105)
precauciones universales Medidas que toman los profesionales de la salud para reducir el riesgo de entrar en contacto con la sangre y otros fluidos corporales.

urethritis Inflammation of the lining of the urethra. (p. 92)
uretritis Inflamación del revestimiento interno de la uretra.

uterus The hollow, muscular, pear-shaped organ in which a fertilized egg develops and grows. (p. 28)
útero Órgano muscular hueco, en forma de pera, en el cual se desarrolla y crece el óvulo fecundado.

V

vagina The hollow, muscular passage leading from the uterus to the outside of the female body. (p. 28)
vagina Canal muscular que comunica el útero con el exterior del cuerpo femenino.

vaginitis A vaginal infection or irritation. (p. 34)
vaginitis Infección o irritación de la vagina.

values The standards and beliefs that are most important to you and that help you decide what is right and wrong. (p. 14)
valores Normas y creencias que son muy importantes para ti, y que te ayudan a decidir lo que es bueno y malo.

viral load The number of virus particles circulating in the body. (p. 107)
carga viral Cantidad de partículas de un virus que circulan en el cuerpo.

Z

zygote The united egg and sperm. (p. 65)
cigoto Óvulo y espermatozoide ya unidos.

Index

Page numbers for key terms are printed in **boldface** type.
Page numbers for illustrations, maps, and charts are printed in *italics*.

Page numbers for key terms are printed in **boldface** type.
Page numbers for illustrations, maps, and charts are printed in *italics*.

Acknowledgments

Note: *Every effort has been made to locate the copyright owner of material reprinted in this book. Omissions brought to our attention will be corrected in subsequent editions.*

Staff Credits

The people who made up the ***Pearson Health*** team—representing design services, editorial, editorial services, education technology, market research, marketing services, planning and budgeting, product planning, production services, publishing processes, and rights and permissions—are listed below. Boldface type denotes the core team members.

Jennifer Angel, Alan Asarch, Amy C. Austin, Charlene Barr, **Neil Benjamin,** Peggy Bliss, Stephanie Bradley, **Jim Brady, Diane Braff,** Lisa Brown, Maureen Griffin, Christian Henry, **Sarah G. Jensen,** Linda D. Johnson, Alicia Lankowski, **James Lonergan, Zareh MacPherson Artinian, Dotti Marshall, Lauren McDonough, Maria Milczarek, Natania Mlawer,** Julia F. Osborne, Jennifer Parker, Alice Pihuleac, Nick Raducanu, **Paul M. Ramos, Logan Schmidt,** Malti Sharma, Aileen Shuman, Melissa Shustyk, **Nancy Smith,** Cindy Strowman, **Elizabeth Tustian,** Amanda M. Watters, **Berkley Wilson**

Additional Credits AARTPACK, Inc., Dan Breslin, Laura J. Chadwick, Liz Good, Russ Lappa, Ellen Levinger, Brent McKenzie, Laurel Smith, Emily Soltanoff, Linda B. Thornhill

Illustration

Young Sook Cho: 25, 35; **John Edwards, Inc.:** 21, 22, 32, 28-29, 65, 66, 81.
All additional art created by AARTPACK, Inc.

Photography

Photo Research AARTPACK, Inc.

Photo locators denoted as follows: Top (T), Center (C), Bottom (B), Left (L), Right (R), Background (Bkgd)

Cover Bkgd Ben Welsh/Corbis; **TL** Yellowj/Shutterstock; **BL** Fuse/Thinkstock

Table of Contents iii Pearson Education; **iv** (BL) BananaStock/Jupiter Images, (BR) Comstock Images/age fotostock, (T) Egidia Degrassi/Fotolia LLC; **1** (BL) Syracuse Newspapers/Suzanne Dunn/The Image Works, (BR) Thinkstock/Jupiter Images, (T) Hemera Technologies/Alamy.

Chapter 1 Pages 2-3, Stockbyte/Thinkstock; **3** Pearson Education; **4** Bananastock/Fotosearch; **5** (BL) Wang Leng/Getty Images, (BR) Thomas Tolstrup/Getty Images, (T) Bananastock/Fotosearch; **6** Creasource/Corbis; **7** Steve Smith/Getty Images; **8** Nico Kai/Getty images; **9** Egidia Degrassi/Fotolia LLC; **10** (L) Richard Haynes/Pearson Education, (R) Comstock/PictureQuest; **12** (L) Michael Newman/PhotoEdit, (R) Tom & Dee Ann McCarthy/Corbis, (C) Stockbyte/SuperStock; **14** John Lund/Marc Romanelli/Blend Images/Corbis; **15** SW Productions/Getty Images; **16** Comstock Images/age Fotostock.

Photography *(continued)*

Chapter 2 Pages 18-19, Stewart Cohen/Getty Images; **19** Pearson Education; **20** Joel Sartore/Getty images; **22** David M. Phillips/Science Source; **23** Bananastock/Fotosearch; **24** Syracuse Newspapers/Suzanne Dunn/The Image Works; **26** Aaron Haupt/Science Source; **27** SW Productions/Getty Images; **30** Andersen Ross/Getty Images; **31** RubberBall Productions/Imagestate; **33** Thinkstock/Jupiter Images; **34** Pixland/age Fotostock; **35** Robynmac/Fotolia LLC; **36** Pete Saloutos/Corbis.

Chapter 3 Pages 38-39, Michael Pole/Corbis; **39** Pearson Education; **40** BananaStock/Jupiter Images; **41** Chuck Savage/Corbis; **42** Pictorial Press Ltd/Alamy; **45** Janine Wiedel Photolibrary/Alamy; **46** Loretta Ray/Getty images; **47** Claudiu Paizan/Fotolia LLC; **48** SW Productions/Getty Images; **49** Jeff Greenberg/Age Fotostock; **50** Brad Wilson/Getty images; **52** Massachusetts Citizens for Children; **54** Comstock/SuperStock; **56** Richard Heinzen/SuperStock.

Chapter 4 Pages 58-59, Spencer Grant/Photo Researchers; **59** Pearson Education; **60** Karen Grigoryan/Shutterstock; **61** Zigy Kaluzny-Charles Thatcher/Getty images; **62** Nick Dolding/Getty images; **63** Trinette Reed/PictureQuest; **64** (B) David M. Phillips/Science Source, (T) Michael Newman/PhotoEdit; **67** (B) Petit Format/Photo Researchers, (T) Claude Edelmann/Photo Researchers; **68** Siede Preis/Getty Images; **69** Plush Studios/PictureQuest; **70** (L) Thinkstock/Fotosearch, (R) Bananastock/PictureQuest; **71** Image Source/Alamy; **72** BSIP/UIG/Getty Images; **73** David J. Green - lifestyle themes/Alamy; **74** Richard Haynes/Pearson Education; **76** Spencer Grant/PhotoEdit; **77** Rubberball/Getty Images; **78** (B) Keith Brofsky/Getty Images, (T) White Packert/The Image Bank/Getty Images, (C) Michael Newman/PhotoEdit; **79** (L) Michael Newman/PhotoEdit, (R) Cervical Barrier Advancement Society; **80** (B) Custom Medical Stock Photo/CMSP, (C) Olivier Voisin/Science Source, (T) Ray Ellis/Photo Researchers; **83** Tom Grill/Corbis; **84** Supershoot images/Getty images.

Chapter 5 Pages 86-87, Cindy Charles/PhotoEdit; **87** Pearson Education; **88** BananaStock/Superstock; **89** Bob Daemmrich/The Image Works; **90** (B) Brand X Pictures/Fotosearch, (T) Will Hart/PhotoEdit; **91** Roy Morsch/Corbis; **92** Marmaduke St. John/Alamy; **93** (C) NIH/CMSP, (L) Eye of Science/Photo Researchers, (R) Alfred Pasieka/Photo Researchers; **94** (B) Slate River Productions/Alamy, (T) Meredun Animal Health Ltd/Photo Researchers; **95** (B) Eye of Science/Photo Researchers, (T) David M. Phillips/Photo Researchers; **96** (B) Logical Images/CMSP, (R) Prints and Photographs Division, Library of Congress, (T) Dr. Kari Lounatmaa/Photo Researchers; **97** ColorBlind Images/Blend Images/Corbis; **98** Hemera Technologies/Alamy; **99** NIBSC/Photo Researchers; **100** Pearson Education; **101** Lawrence Manning/Corbis; **102** Glowimages6/Alamy; **103** Sean Sprague/The Image Works; **104** E. Dygas/Getty images; **105** Guy Cali/Corbis; **106** (L) Klaus Guldbrandsen/Photo Researchers, (R) Rachel Frank/Alamy; **107** Michael Newman/PhotoEdit; **108** MICHAEL DWYER/AP Images.